The Night of the Comet

SEBASTIANO VASSALLI

★

THE NIGHT
OF THE COMET

Translated by John Gatt

CARCANET

First published in Great Britain 1989 by
Carcanet Press Limited
208–212 Corn Exchange Buildings
Manchester M4 3BQ

Translated from *La notte della cometa*
Copyright © 1984 Giulio Einaudi editore s.p.a., Turin
This translation copyright © 1989 John Gatt

British Library Cataloguing in Publication Data

Vassalli, Sebastiano, *1941-*
    The night of the comet.
    I. Title   II. La notte della cometa.
    English
    853'.914[F]

    ISBN 0-85635-773-1

The publisher acknowledges financial assistance from
the Arts Council of Great Britain

Typeset in 11pt Bembo by Bryan Williamson, Manchester
Printed in England by SRP Ltd, Exeter

The people of Italy sing no more
You *parvenu*! You are our ruin.

Marradi, September 1983. The Ristorante Albergo Lamone, where I've been staying for a week now, has a leaflet saying: 'Hotel equipped to modern standards. Genuine traditional cuisine. Tuscan and Romagnol specialities. Quality service for weddings, banquets, parties etc. Game, trout, mushrooms, Marradi's own *pecorino* cheese, chestnut gateau. Tuscan and Romagnol wines.' The bedrooms occupy two floors and overlook the railway goods yard on one side and, on the other side, an avenue of horse-chestnuts named after one Baccarini, but customarily referred to as 'the station avenue'. In one of these rooms the poet Dino Campana and the writer Sibilla Aleramo spent the Christmas night of 1916. It may have been the room I am now in, or another one. Who knows. The hotel has had alterations to the internal walls but is unchanged in its external structure, and is very probably of an age with the Florence to Faenza railway line: this was opened in 1893 amid great popular festivity and in the presence of His Highness the Duke of Genoa, representing Umberto I of Savoy, King of Italy 'by the grace of God and the will of the Nation'.

The tourist guides say little about Marradi: 328 metres above sea level, five thousand inhabitants (but at the beginning of the century there were far more, almost twice as many), a few shrines in the vicinity, remains of feudal towers...Just a country town on the highway, with no special cultural or linguistic features. Only the buildings in Piazza Scalelle still speak of an age when Marradi was the little capital of 'Tuscan Romagna' on the frontier between two States: the Grand Duchy of Tuscany and the State of the Church. The landscape, which is pleasing, presents no particularly striking prospects or characteristics. The outline of the mountains is 'gentle' yet 'severe', as Campana said. The sky is bright, the vegetation varied: but that is of a piece with the beauty of Apennine and Italian scenery in general. Italy is all enchantment.

From my window I see 'azure mountains', 'strata upon strata' of rocks, fanning out like the pages of the book of the universe: and I recall Dino's words, spoken to Sibilla: 'This is a place where I've suffered greatly. My blood has left its marks among the rocks up there.' – I don't really know what I'm looking for in Marradi. There are no papers here, no documents – everything was destroyed during the last war – and even if I found some hundred-year-old still capable of memory and speech, what could he tell me about Dino Campana: that he was the village idiot? For that is the one and only truth; but the truth is not uttered. Maybe, I reflect, I've come all this way merely to see the places he loved, to seek out that blood among the rocks; perhaps I hoped to find his statue. Of course, his statue. The life-size statue of the Mad Poet. In Bacchic posture. Not unlike, except in garb, those monuments to the Unknown Soldier which are to be found in just about every village and small town, near the railway station or in the middle of piazzas appropriately dedicated to the Fallen. Heroes. Saints. Poets. Navigators. To Us! (Such, rightly, was the cry of D'Annunzio's legionaries and the Duce's *squadristi*, with which, carried away by their own rhetoric, they laid bare invidious truths.)

The monument to Campana has not yet been built. It will come: but first, time and rhetoric must have their due. From village idiot to hero is a long jump. For the time being, he's been given a plaque, he's had a street named after him, his very own literary prize has been set up in his name. The Dino Campana literary prize. Panel of judges: Giorgio Saviane, Claudio Marabini, Aldo Rossi, Lorenzo Ricchi and other celebrities. It may not seem much, but it is. Thirty years ago, when a journalist, Sergio Zavoli, came to Marradi on Campana's trail, the first thing he was told by the hard-faced men in the piazza was: 'He was a madman, that's all there is to it.' But Zavoli didn't give up the quest. In the civic centre he interviewed the deputy mayor Leo Consolini and the retired municipal secretary, the *cavaliere* Bucivini Capecchi, a contemporary of Dino's. '*Zavoli: Cavaliere* Bucivini, has anyone reproached the local authority for not having done much to honour the memory of Dino Campana? *Bucivini Capecchi*: As a matter of fact, during one council meeting there were some councillors who protested. They protested at the idea of honouring this Dino Campana, because some of them said he was a precursor of Fascism... *Zavoli*: Indeed! *Bucivini Capecchi*: ... whereas we contemporaries of his can prove that he had absolutely nothing to do with it, he took no interest in such matters! *Leo Consolini*: Besides, the evidence that the *Comune* of Marradi did commit itself to honouring Dino Campana is there. Look: for two consecutive years, that is, in 1952 and 1953, 500,000 lire were budgeted for the purpose. But the administrative council of the province saw fit to annul that provision on the grounds that the Marradi *Comune* was running a deficit! Apart from that, just to show you the *Comune's* determination to give the poet the honour due to him, the judgement, let us say, of great men and eminent institutions of learning was sought: the writer Ardengo Soffici, the Senator Emilio Sereni, the Accademia della Crusca, the Accademia dei Lincei, the Deputation for National History. I have the evidence here, in this folder.'

The replies from the Academies and great men betray embarrassment and compunction, and favour, in principle, any kind of celebration. They deny that Campana was a 'precursor of Fascism' and give assurances that there can be no objections against him. 'Dear Comrade,' writes Senator Emilio Sereni to the Communist mayor of Marradi, who has consulted him over the naming of a street, 'I think it is right to name a street in your town after Dino Campana.

'Dino Campana is undoubtedly a name that carries authority in modern poetry and has now become part of literary history.

'There are no political reservations about him. Moreover his madness clears him of any responsibility for any political stance of his. And, in any case, he was never avowedly reactionary.

'It would be as well to have the street named by a Tuscan writer. Try writing to Romano Bilenchi in Florence to ask if he would give a speech for the occasion. Signed: Sereni.'

I'm sorting out the skeletons in the cupboard. 'Fanny' Luti and Giovanni Campana, who wanted to 'settle' their son ('for his own good,' they said) and calmed down only when they knew he'd been locked up in an asylum, permanently. His uncle and guardian Torquato, who, like the 'worthy scholar' that he was, composed the epigraph and dictated it to him. Papini and Soffici, the fashionable intellectuals, who taught him humility and the rules of the literary game. The 'howling jackals' of Marradi and the 'jackals of the cupola', that is, the Florentine littérateurs, who regarded him as a 'natural', a colourful character out of local folklore. The D'Annunzian Rina Faccio, Aleramo (an anagram, aptly, of *amorale*), as she called herself in the world of letters, who in the summer of 1917, when all male Italians were at the front, counted the months she had spent 'in a state of sanctity' and laid the blame on Campana. The critic Bino Binazzi, seriously convinced that, if Dino was to be famous as a poet, he must first of all be a famous madman. The electrician-psychiatrists who turned him into the electric man 'Dino Edison'. The other psychiatrist, Pariani, who, for the sake of writing a hopelessly mediocre book on the relationship between genius and madness, tormented him with exhausting (and fruitless) interrogations from 1926 to 1930. The critic Enrico Falqui, who lovingly embalmed his memory and in a good Christian spirit censored and corrected his letters: for instance, 'Osteria della Musa' [The Muse's Inn] in place of 'Osteria della Mussa' [The Pussy

Inn]. Attilio Vallecchi, the publisher, who cleaned up the *Canti Orfici*, excising some indecent pieces. And then, besides, the nameless grave-diggers, the gratuitous liars, the disinterested denigrators... Will it suffice to say, with Dino, that 'they're all cover'd with the boy's blood', 'marked to be picked out on the day of justice'?

I look out of the window again. 'The haze of gold-dust that enveloped the town seemed suddenly sublimated into a blood-sacrifice. When? I took the blood-red gleams of sunset to bear me its farewell.' I've been fourteen years in search of the truth about Dino Campana's life, piecing it together one fragment at a time, cleansing each fragment of the encrustation of falsehood, of legend, on which time had already conferred the patina of authenticity... Now the quest is over and Dino's life is there, all of it, in a suitcase crammed with notes and photocopies, propped up against the radiator in this hotel room, perhaps the very room in which he spent his last Christmas at Marradi... The entire life of a man considered by his contemporaries an anomaly of nature, someone who 'hadn't grasped at all what ordinary living is' and was simply a poet. But perhaps it is true that poets belong to another species, a 'primitive', 'barbarous' species, a species which has always been extinct and which is yet forever capable of rebirth like the phoenix of Araby. Real poets, I mean: not littérateurs or writers of poems, but only those through whom poetry speaks. The unicorns, the freaks.

Campana, Dino Carlo Giuseppe, is born at 2.30 p.m. on 20 August 1885 in Marradi, within the Province of Florence, to Giovanni, a primary school teacher, and Francesca Luti, housewife. His constellation is Leo, with Sagittarius in the ascendant. His horoscope speaks of his being conscious of his worth; of his extremely strong aspiration to excel; of his will to dominate without using violent means; of scant, or at least limited, consideration for others; of intense but ephemeral passions.

Father and mother are comfortably off. He, Giovanni Campana, is thirty-eight and was born in Marradi. She, Francesca, known as 'Fanny', is fifteen years younger than her husband; she's from Comeana, near Florence, and has spent her childhood and adolescence in a boarding-school run by nuns. Like many of her contemporaries who entered upon marriage and motherhood from an almost monastic experience of life, 'Fanny' has a hard time adapting to her new station and, besides, seems dissatisfied with her husband, who – for some unknown reason – does not content or appeal to her. She is an Emma Bovary without the courage to commit adultery, or perhaps without the opportunity, who gradually retreats into a shell consisting of her memories of school, religious practices, a chastity guarded and justified by migraines, indispositions, lenten fasts and abstinences, penances, vows... She is a woman disaffected with the milieu in which she lives and the people with whom she lives, but who feels there is no escape and asks only to be left in peace. She'll see to the laundry, the shopping, she'll keep the family together, sacrificing herself in silence. She'll stay at her post, but – she won't go as far as feigning an attachment to her husband and to her son which she does not feel...

Fanny Luti Campana's matrimonial crisis comes to a head during her second pregnancy and manifests itself, after the birth of her second child, Manlio, in her rejection of Dino, which substitutes for and symbolizes her rejection of her husband. As for the latter, 'Fanny' confines herself to denying her favours: she wants no more pregnancies and considers conjugal relations illicit except for purposes of procreation, 'giving children to God', as she was taught at convent school. (Perhaps, or rather, probably, she takes no pleasure in sex: but who knows?) These are in fact the years, roughly between 1890 and 1895, when the school-teacher Giovanni Campana begins to complain of 'neurasthenic disorders' of an unmistakable kind (irritability, insomnia, abrupt changes of mood) and to treat himself with herbal teas and infusions supplied by the pharmacist in Marradi. Until, overdoing things as always, he takes the train one Sunday and gets himself admitted to the asylum at Imola, to the care of that same Dr Brugia to whom, a decade later, he sends his son Dino: 'See that you cure my son as you cured me...'

A patriot and doughty champion of 'the Italians' moral and civil primacy', Giovanni Campana is in many ways a typical representative of his generation, shaped by the rhetoric and the enthusiasms of the Risorgimento. He is an agnostic but not an atheist, like the writer De Amicis; he is a republican yet devoted to the monarchy, like the statesman Crispi; a materialist but a firm believer in genius, like the scientist Lombroso... At school, he delights in teaching that man is a marriage of two machines: a steam engine, which is the respiratory system, and a hydraulic engine, which is the circulatory system. 'But what about the soul, sir?' 'That's a third machine, the nervous system, an electrical engine.' Though of a mild and somewhat retiring temperament, school-teacher Campana has a trait which has already been mentioned and which will be a determining factor in the life of his son: when faced with a problem, he is absolute and excessive; he will not accept just any solution, as most people will, but will pursue, among all the possible solutions, the definitive and 'final' one... Other family members whose memory has been preserved are Dino's paternal grandfather and his mother's brother and sister, Lorenzo and Egle Luti: but these were not prominent in Dino's life. Not so his father's brothers, each of whom has a compartment to himself in my suitcase. These were, beginning with the youngest, Uncle Torquato, Uncle Francesco, and the Mad Uncle.

Let us start with the last-mentioned. The existence of the

Mad Uncle, probably older than the others, probably the first-born, was the great secret of the Campana family: a secret so well guarded that the Mad Uncle's name, all memory of him, everything to do with him, has disappeared. But he did exist, and he was the tangible manifestation of a spectre – the spectre of heredity – which haunted the lives and fortunes of all the Campanas, not only Dino's. I lighted on it by chance during the winter of 1982 at the State Archive in Florence, while rummaging through those boxes of legal documents which the archivists call by a terrible metaphor 'lunatic files'. I had the good fortune to find the folder regarding the admission into the San Salvi asylum, on 9 April 1909, of 'Campana Dino son of Giovanni, aged 23, single, born and resident in Marradi, well-to-do', and, tucked away inside the folder and forgotten, the 'information sheet' made out by the health officer of the *Comune* of domicile. In answer to the question regarding the 'physical and moral causes' of Campana's madness, he writes: 'Heredity – Alcohol'; and against the question 'whether any of the patient's relatives are or have been deranged, and which ones', the following words, in which a man's life receives its final reckoning: 'An uncle of the patient's died in an Asylum.'

'Lunatic files'... One box-file after another, folder upon folder, dust added to dust, the inquirer descends into a chasm compared to which Dante's Hell or Orcagna's Last Judgement seem, and are, but trifles. Here you find none of Dante's 'throngs' or 'people' or 'hosts', there is no collective abstraction as background and frame for a few individual dramas. Each of the 'insane' steps forward with name, case-history, and specific sentence: and there are thousands and tens of thousands of them. They are diagnosed as having 'insane apoplexy', 'circular insanity', 'periodic disturbances' (in the case of women), 'melancholia' or, more frequently, 'senile melancholia', 'progressive paralysis', 'hypochondria', 'involutive psychosis', 'alcoholism', 'epileptic insanity', 'dementia praecox': most frequently 'dementia praecox'. The committal orders by Mayors and Royal Governors – who, from 1904, were charged with authorizing the admission of the 'insane' into the public institutions – are offhand as to the grounds for admission. They state that the patient 'vociferates', that he 'drinks', that he 'molests women on the public highway'; that he is 'temperamentally unstable' or 'unstable in his or her affections' (you can land in an asylum for adultery, especially if you're a woman); that he's 'disorderly', 'careless', 'forgetful', 'depressed'; that he 'quarrels with his family'; that he 'raves'. Once admitted into an asylum, the patient is kept under observation for a period of time which, by the law of 14 February 1904, No 36, 'may not exceed one

month in all'. The ritual of admitting the patient 'definitively' or releasing him because of 'inadequate grounds'
takes place in court; but the real arbiters of the destiny of
those suspected of insanity are ultimately only the psychiatrists. They are called upon to convict or to acquit on the
basis of their individual good sense and of a book-lore which
Benedetto Croce is already calling 'a pseudo-science', 'a
hotch-potch', 'mere empiricism'. What's to be done? If in
doubt, the psychiatrists declare the patient insane: adhering
to the golden rule that a sane person in an asylum does
nobody any harm, while a lunatic at large is always a risk
for the doctor, who would have to account for any mis-
demeanour he may commit... Perhaps two-thirds of the
cases I looked at, over the period from 1906 to 1918, end
with the 'definitive admission' of the person suspected of
insanity: that is, a full life-sentence. Recovery, rehabilitation
within society, are essentially theoretical outcomes. For two
reasons: first and foremost because living in an asylum
brings on that special form of insanity that the psychiatrists
of the day call 'institutional insanity' and which is caused –
the manuals say – 'by segregation, idleness, and the company of lunatics'. Secondly, because anyone who has left
an asylum remains ever after at the mercy of the first little
urchin that jeers at him in the street, of the first policeman
whom he forgets to salute, of the first relative who wants
him out of the way. Whatever he does, the least that can
befall him is to find himself back in the madhouse after
going through the whole business again, from 'provisional
admission' to permanent confinement. And to end up by
adapting to a life compared with which even a prison is in
some respects an enviable environment.

Of the Mad Uncle, nobody knows a thing. But since Dino is heir to his reputation, both within the family and among the people of Marradi, I think it's right and legitimate to attribute to the uncle that part of the 'Campana legend' which cannot be attributed to the nephew, and which concerns the molesting of the women of Marradi. Let us therefore render to Dino that which is Dino's, and to the Mad Uncle that which is the Mad Uncle's. For instance, the exhibitionist antics near the bridge over the Lamone, with a refrain to match: 'I'm Campana [Bell] and this is my clapper,' the Madman chants at all the women who pass that way, then whips open his coat and shows them something. Or the harassing of shepherd girls on the mountains; or the attempts at coupling with women busy in the open-air laundry, taking them by surprise and from the rear. Whatever his specific disorder (possibly 'circular', or 'apoplectic', or some other sort) the Mad Uncle is tormented by sex, and this is one of the few things that we can definitely say about him. The others concern the date of his death (certainly prior to 9 April 1909) and that of his confinement in the asylum (certainly later than 4 August 1904): almost to the end of his days, the Madman lives with his family, despite the hullabaloos he causes and despite Fanny's hostility.

Let us verify those dates. That the Mad Uncle died before 9 April 1909 is down in black and white on the 'information sheet' attached to court proceedings regarding Dino, and is therefore, beyond doubt. That he lived at home until

August 1904 emerges though indirectly, from another unquestionable source: the Levy Register of the Florence military district for the class of 1885. This records that from 4 January to 4 August of 1904 Dino Campana is an infantry officer cadet, that is, at the Modena Military Academy. The cavalry have their Academy at Pinerolo; the navy at Leghorn. The military career of Dino Campana, 'volunteer in the 40th Infantry Regiment (Officer cadet) registered 1st category class of 1883' is completely subsumed within those two dates. On 4 April 1904 – the Levy Register reads – Dino becomes a corporal; on 4 August 'his status as officer cadet lapses because of his failing the examination for the rank of sergeant' but he is allowed a 'good conduct certificate'. His personal characteristics are recorded as: 'height 1.68 metres', 'complexion pink', 'hair colour chestnut shape straight', 'eyes chestnut', 'teeth sound', 'distinguishing marks mole on right cheek'. And now to return to his uncle. It is absolutely certain that Dino would not have been admitted into the Military Academy if a relative of his had been declared 'insane' and confined in an asylum. There is no certainty, but there is a likelihood, that the Mad Uncle's presence was endured in Marradi for the sake of his nephew's career; and that matters came to a head for him precisely as a result of that career falling through...

As the nineteenth century ends and the twentieth begins the Campanas are obsessed with the Madman in their midst, with the spectre of heredity. They all watch themselves and one another for symptoms of that disorder which has struck once already and can therefore strike again: all display special curiosity about their relatives' 'peculiarities'. A tinge of madness is perceived both in the lawyer, Francesco, sub-Procurator Royal at the High Court in Florence, and in the primary school teacher Torquato, though he is the most extrovert of the Campanas and the best known in the Marradi area. (Torquato, the memoirs say, is a 'scholar' who writes 'brief verse compositions' to celebrate weddings, anniversaries and festivities. He seems normal enough to talk to: but isn't artistic aptitude in itself a symptom of deviance, according to Lombroso, Nordau and other scientific authorities?) As for the other school-teacher, Giovanni, it is common knowledge that he suffered from neurasthenia after the birth of his second son and that he managed to recover; that he is – or is at least considered to be – an asylum survivor. It's a well-known story. One Sunday morning, in one of the years between 1895 and 1900, the primary school teacher Giovanni Campana of Marradi presents himself of his own accord at the Imola mental asylum, where a certain Dr Brugia listens to his account of his disorder and prescribes two powders, mysterious to us (valerian? bromide?) but miraculous to him. The effects of those powders on the school-teacher's 'psyche' are so beneficial as to lead him to regard himself cured by a miracle of science: which, thanks to Brugia, has restored his sleep and peace of mind and body. So, when the family problem arises of his eldest son not getting on with his mother, the teacher Campana has no hesitation in sending him to the asylum in Imola for the miracle to be repeated, and he writes Brugia a letter which the latter puts straight into Dino's clinical file, since it concerns the father's neurasthenic disorders, that is, a matter of heredity... 'See that you cure my son as you cured me,' writes the school-teacher to 'his' doctor. And he adds: 'This son of mine has never been physically ill, up to the age of fifteen he's always been a bit reserved, but always well-behaved, obedient and sensible in dealing with his own affairs, though somewhat untidy. His mother is a healthy, energetic, intelligent and spirited woman. After the delivery she herself nursed him quite happily and was proud of the sturdiness of her fine baby.'

Let us have a philological look at this letter. Campana calls the babe-in-arms *bell'allievo*, an unusual expression harking back to the Latin *alĕre*, meaning 'to feed, nurse'; which shows that he does not pick his words casually. Let us examine further those four adjectives ('healthy, energetic, intelligent, spirited') with which Giovanni sketches what amounts to a cameo of his wife, a distinct and pronounced portrait that hints broadly at the relations between husband and wife at the time when the letter was penned, that is, in September 1906... Now content with his powders, his urges now definitely quelled, Giovanni regards his wife with respect and trepidation: he says she is 'healthy', that is, free from hereditary taints; that she is 'energetic', meaning that she gives the orders; that she is 'intelligent', in that she knows what she wants and how to go about achieving it; that she is 'spirited' (*risentita* in the Italian), with more than an overtone of 'resentful' and 'quarrelsome'. And it is noticeable that the portrait, though positively presented, completely lacks all the feminine and specifically maternal qualities of sensitivity, understanding, tenderness and suchlike; but, a little further along, there comes a fifth adjective: 'proud'.

Another picture, a sketch which helps us to understand the mother's character and her future conflicts with her son, emerges from a recollection of Fanny's about Dino as an infant: 'Quiet, fine-looking, chubby, curly-haired, intelligent, at two years of age he could recite the *Ave Maria* in

French, I was the envy of all around me.' – So let us imagine Piazza Scalelle in Marradi with its town hall, its arcades, its shops, its café tables, people going to and fro; Fanny in her outdoor clothes with her parasol standing by the arcade; in front of her, the arch-priest Don Domenico Cavina who smiles as he leans forward over the 'fine and chubby' infant, prompting him to recite his prayers. A few steps away, some of the working-class women hover, listening to the little polyglot. Fanny feels she is the object of admiration, and rejoices inwardly. The limited French she learnt at convent school (two or three prayers and a vocabulary of a hundred-odd words, just enough for a young lady of the nineteenth century to confide a secret to her best friend) is one of the things that most sets her apart from these Marradi bumpkins... She calls her infant *mon petit chou*, coaxes him to greet the arch-priest: '*Salue monsieur l'archiprêtre...*'

Early in 1888, all the Marradi Campanas move to their new house at No 1, Via Pescetti, the one that still belongs to their heirs and on which the *Comune* has placed a plaque with an inscription devised – I believe – by Falqui: 'In this, which was his house...Dino Campana composed...' It is a fine three-storey house with a raised ground floor and a large garden; on the ground floor live the older generation with the Mad Uncle, then Torquato's family on the first floor, and Giovanni's on the second. Fanny discovers she is pregnant again, and a few months later gives birth to her second child, Manlio. Dino is left to his own devices: he is rejected by his mother. During his infancy, he is looked after partly by his Uncle Torquato and Aunt Giovanna and partly by two sisters of mature years, Marianna and Barberina Bianchi, obscurely connected to the Campanas. The Bianchi sisters are churchy spinsters; the younger of them, Marianna, has the task of going round from house to house gathering alms for the church. They disapprove of Fanny's behaviour towards her first child. 'After the birth of Manlio, her pet,' Torquato's wife, Giovanna Diletti, writes later, 'Dino took second place, or rather, third place. Ninni (Manlio), always Ninni, only Ninni. Marianna even more than Barberina was fond of Dino. When she came to my house collecting money for the church she would ask me, how are they getting on upstairs? and she'd vent her feelings. Can you imagine, she would say, a poor little lad whose mother says to him when they go out for a walk: "Now you, Dino, walk along to Palazzuolo street (the Marradi slum area), we (Fanny and Manlio) will go another way"?

Dino starts going to school, and Marianna and Barberina clothe him out of their savings because they're upset to see the difference – which is obvious even in what he wears – between him and his younger brother; for Fanny drapes him, right from childhood, 'in the ugliest clothes, or his father's cast-offs'. ('In any case,' says she, 'he's so untidy!') Of his progress at school nothing is known: registers, records, buildings, everything was destroyed during the last war, when Marradi happened to be on the so-called 'Gothic Line'. But he probably does well. His conduct is less good. Manlio Campana, interviewed in the early Fifties, speaks of his brother as a child who found it hard to get on with his fellows ('I sought his company but perhaps he was not so eager for mine... or anyone else's') and who was frequently punished by the school-master: most likely, that is, by his Uncle Torquato. A school photograph of this period shows the future author of the *Canti Orfici* among a great number of schoolchildren under the charge of Torquato Campana. Judging by the age of the children – all eight or nine years old – the photograph might be of primary class three, that is, the 1893-94 school year...

Between primary school and *liceo* – the only category of school from which you can proceed to a Military Academy – you have to pass through the so-called *ginnasio*: five years divided into a 'lower' level of three years which will later be termed 'middle school', and an 'upper' level. Dino spends this time at boarding-school, the Salesian Institute in Faenza, which is the best available at this time and in this part of Romagna to prepare boys from the country for the *liceo*. He starts there in the autumn of 1896 – the year of the Italian colonial defeat at Adowa – and stays there, except for the long summer holidays and the much briefer Christmas and Easter holidays, continuously until the summer of 1900 – the year in which King Umberto I is assassinated. He goes straight into the second form, having passed an entrance examination of which no records have survived. He has to take two other examinations, at the end of his third- and fifth-form years, at the 'E. Torricelli' Royal *Ginnasio-Liceo* in Faenza, as the Italian State does not recognize qualifications issued by priests. His marks for the third form of the *ginnasio* (with 10 as maximum) are: 6 and 7 in Italian, 8 and 7 in Latin, 6 and 8 in French, 6 in geography, 8 in arithmetic. And for the fifth form: 7 and 8 in Italian, 7 and 6 in Latin, 6 and 6 in Greek, 8 in history, 6 in geography, 6 in mathematics, 7 in natural history, 9 and 7 in French.

What is life like in a religious boarding-school during the final years of the nineteenth century? According to Benito

Mussolini, who was a boarder in this same Salesian Institute from 1892 to 1894 for his third and fourth primary forms, there can only be one answer: terrible. The Duce's memoirs speak of the Institute as a boys' concentration camp: with 'cubicles' in which anyone who disobeys his 'superiors' is locked up, with fierce guard-dogs released in the grounds at night, frequent and sadistic application of such punishments as being deprived of food, detention during games periods, beatings in public. But Mussolini was a 'third class' boarder, and his evidence, while certainly honest and indicative, is also limited to certain aspects of a reality which, for obvious reasons, he could not grasp in its entirety...

So let us consider boarding-schools and 'class'. Religious boarding-schools at the turn of the nineteenth century are either too exclusive to admit boys from the middle and lower middle classes or else are divided into 'classes', like trains. The parent entering his son may choose to pay for him to have special treatment (first class), ordinary treatment (second class), or economy treatment (third class). In this last case the boarder is placed in the so-called 'foundlings'' dormitory, where the religious institution houses boys who have been orphaned or abandoned by their parents and are maintained out of charity and hired out as mourners to follow the funerals of the wealthy. Each class has its own dormitory and receives board and services proportionate to the fees paid. Tuition, games and worship are common to all on an equal basis – or they are supposed to be: but it goes without saying that no master will bother himself excessively over a third-class pupil ('After all, he'll only become a labourer...'). And it goes without saying that there are also two different weights and two different measures when it comes to meting out punishment. But what makes the system inhuman is its sheer blatancy, the fact that every child can, and is in fact bound to, compare what is on his own plate with what is on his neighbour's, and that every aspect of life within the institution is based in the first place on this hard discipline. 'At table,' Mussolini recalls, 'we boys used to sit in three sections. I always had to sit down at the end and eat with the poorest. I might be able to forget the ants in the bread of the third class boarders. But the fact that we children were divided into classes still makes my soul smart.'

Religion is imposed in 'oppressive and terrifying' ways. Mass at daybreak every day. (Two Masses on Sundays, one 'ordinary', the other 'festive'.) Prayers on waking, at the beginning and end of lessons, before and after meals, at bedtime. Edifying books read out twice a day during meals. The common tendency, at Faenza and everywhere in institutions of this type, is to regard the boarder as a reserve seminarist, a sort of casual monk who will eventually leave. It's for this reason he is made to recite so many prayers and hear so many masses, to suffice, should he forsake his religion, for the rest of his days...

Sexual repression, the final goal of all teaching and all educational activity, is effected in many ways. Chemically, to begin with. Twice a day the boarder unwittingly swallows bromides and sedatives, whose side-effects are also considered beneficial: the subject becomes more docile and calm, his conduct in class improves and so does his progress. Religion brings in the sixth and ninth commandments with the certainty of hell for habitual fornicators; medical science attests that so-called 'impure actions' lead to loss of eyesight, memory and reason; physical education and sport are conceived as work-outs, the violent release of an excess of energy which if retained could lead to sinful thoughts; morality is administered by the 'spiritual assistant' exclusively in the form of prohibitions against keeping one's hands in one's pockets, 'touching oneself', staying too long in the lavatory, looking at women in the street, thinking about women, thinking...

Dino Campana's experience of life in the Faenza Institute is virtually the opposite of Mussolini's. He is different in temperament, past history and social class: a family that counts among its members magistrates, school-masters and ladies with exotic names cannot lower itself to the point of sending one of its sons to mix with orphans and hired mourners. What he finds at boarding-school is, above all, the sheltered environment and ordered life-style which he has not had at home. He breathes more freely; for the first time, he indulges in childish behaviour and play: he enjoys a belated childhood. His aunt, Giovanna Delitti, pays him a visit one Sunday afternoon, to see him rush 'into the parlour ...in a sweat', clutching a 'top and whipcord': unusual toys for a boy of twelve...Then, he discovers the library. A Michele Campana – unrelated to Dino – who was at the Faenza Institute at the same time, relates that Dino soon gave up his top, as well as the ball-games of his class mates, to recite the passages describing 'the duel between Tancredi and Clorinda beneath the walls of Jerusalem..., the duel between Rinaldo and Sacripante and the even more famous one between Ruggero and Rodomonte' from Tasso's *Gerusalemme Liberata* and Ariosto's *Orlando Furioso*. So Dino reads Tasso, Ariosto, Dante, the literary classics available in 'expurgated' editions – that is, with all the bawdy elements taken out – that he finds in the library of his priestly school. He becomes a model pupil (his marks at school are much better than his examination results) and also obtains good results in the one subject not offered in State schools, that is, religion. In fact, this is the very subject in which his marks denote a growing interest, going from 8 in the *ginnasio* second form to 9 in the third and fourth forms and finally to 10 in the fifth form.

His conduct is good. He is somewhat reserved in temperament; but within this boarding-school milieu school-boy fellowship, youthful enthusiasms, emerging affinities of interest and taste mean that even Dino experiences his first friendships: conceived as 'eternal', but destined, in the event, to fizzle out within a few years, as always with adolescents. So with a certain Giovanni Accardo, and a certain Solumi...

At the end of June of 1900 Dino comes back home to live. His father is surly, but a gentleman. His mother is already as the people of Marradi are to remember her: 'rosary beads in hand, shawl upon her shoulders' (so reports Mariannina Capelli, the poet's cousin). 'Proudly ignoring' (in the words of the same witness) 'her son's concerns, intent only on pursuing him with scoldings, injunctions, punishments and prohibitions' that Dino grudgingly endures, without understanding the reasons for her animosity. He finds her mystical attitudes stupid, her pompousness ridiculous, her reproofs unjust. He dislikes everything about her, but, being now fifteen, he can't solve the problem of living with her by going back to the Palazzuolo street. He gets angry: he asks not to be tormented over the merest trifles (forgetting a pencil on the table, a door not properly shut, a footmark in the entrance hall); he asks to be treated as what he is – a person – and not just to be equated with the nuisance he causes; in short, to be 'respected'...

Faced with this challenge to the domestic arrangements and routine that she has established, Fanny reacts angrily: like the 'healthy' and 'energetic' and, above all, 'spirited' woman that she is. There are scenes, noisy and unseemly, in the Campana household, whose prestige has already been given a hard knock by the exhibitions of the Madman. Now begins Fanny's trial of strength with her husband: she runs away more than once to her own family; she makes black-mailing threats to seek legal separation unless her son leaves the house. Finally, the doubt arises as to Dino's 'insanity'. (Might *he* perhaps be the Madman's heir?)

To depict this situation better, let us imagine a typical incident arising from Dino's 'brutal and morbid impulsiveness' (the words come from his father's letter to Dr Brugia) towards his mother. The lad is tired of finding pictures of the Madonna tucked inside his books and among his papers (Fanny leaves them all over the place, but particularly among the belongings of her elder son, whom she believes to be possessed), so he now turns the contents of his drawers out on the floor and flings out of the window all the holy pictures he can find, while his mother shrieks 'Monster! devil! Anti-Christ!' at him. 'As if it weren't enough dishonour to have your brother in the house,' Fanny cries venomously at her husband, who pleads with her to be patient, to keep quiet. ('The neighbours will hear.') 'This is another cross I have to bear by way of atonement for my sin in marrying you! To have given birth to the Anti-Christ.' (Schoolmaster Giovanni: 'Fanny, I beg you. Control yourself.')

During the school year 1900–01, Dino attends the first year of the *liceo* at the 'E. Torricelli' Royal *Ginnasio-Liceo*, about which there is no detailed information but which is undoubtedly similar to any other *liceo classico* in any other small town in the Italian provinces. (The *liceo classico* is one of the few truly national institutions in early twentieth-century Italy.) Let us picture, then, a building two or three hundred years old, partially modified: *ginnasio* on the ground floor, *liceo* on the first floor. In the courtyard or on the stairway stands the bust of the person after whom the school is named (Torricelli's, of course, in Faenza). The Headmaster is an elderly bureaucrat well-versed in anniversaries, commemorations and local history. There are about thirty teachers, men and women obliged by circumstances to earn their living by acting out a role. This is how it comes about that every *liceo* has its own Pedant, its own Progressive, its Spinster, its Satyr (variation: Homosexual), its Philosopher, its more or less Neglected Genius... Legends about these characters are handed down from generation to generation and involve the Beadles: abject but wily beings, usually engaged in extremely remunerative business on the side or (variation) obscure traffickings with the Pupils. (Cigarettes, pornography, procurement.) The Pupils are divided into two Courses. Course A is exclusively male; Course B is mixed. (Variation: exclusively female.) Unlike the Masters, who last about forty years, the Pupils appear to be ever-changing: but really always stay the same, the Notary's son, who will become a Notary, the Foundry-Owner's son who will become an Advocate, the Advocate's son who will become a Foundry-Owner, the Business-Man's son who will become a Doctor, and so on (and so be it). The teachers (the Characters) are usually short-circuited when they realize they can no longer distinguish the fathers from the sons: dreaded senility sets in, and with it oblivion as regards that select society of Parents and Pupils which for decades the Characters have served, fawned upon, overawed without ever managing to enter, or to gain acceptance.

My suitcase contains a photograph, which many writers on Campana have reproduced, of the first year of the 'E. Torricelli' *liceo* in Faenza of 1900-01. Dino appears, wearing a frown and an incipient moustache: looking a bit older than his nearly sixteen years. A fellow-pupil behind him (possibly Accardo, or Solumi) rests a hand on his shoulder. There are eighteen pupils in all, all male: which means that this is a photograph of Course A. I could try guessing from the faces and postures which is the Notary's son and which the Foundry-Owner's: but that would be just a game. Easier to pick out the characteristics of some already well-developed human types (the debonair, the sophisticate, the lady-killer, the snob) and to imagine the network of relationships, the seamless web of interests, family connections, affinities and rivalries that binds together these scions of the local bourgeoisie, the Notary's son to the Pharmacist's son, the Advocate's son to the Doctor's...

Why do the scions of the Faentine bourgeoisie 'jeer' at Dino Campana, as he himself is to put it in explaining his examination failure and a wasted scholastic year. ('They jeered at me.') During this same year, 1900–01, Dino has problems at home, some of them fairly serious; he 'commutes' between Marradi and Faenza, spending several hours a day in trains or station waiting-rooms; he wears his father's or Uncle Torquato's cast-offs; most significantly, he is certainly an outsider to the boys in the school photograph. On two counts: first, because he does not belong to their society; secondly, because he's come from a boarding-school, where he's completed the entire *ginnasio* programme, whereas the others have always been here, they've been together for five years if not for ten, from the first year of primary school...How many other former boarding-school pupils like Dino appear in the photograph? Who knows? Possibly, none, possibly one – the one resting his hand on Dino's shoulder. In Dino's encounter with the Faenza *liceo*, then, we have to take into account the unwelcoming attitude of the young members of the local bourgeoisie, their unwillingness to fraternize with a naïve, gauche, shy, proud lad from the hills; but since, for someone to be 'jeered' at – that is, systematically and continually derided – there must be some specific pretext or reason, it is my belief that the *liceo* boy Campana is guilty of some *faux pas* with the girls in Course B or perhaps with one in particular – that Francesca B. ('Francesca B., sinner') whose name he is to find, in ten years time, carved on a wall in the shrine of St Francis at La Verna. ('At the sight of the simple figures of love her heart had opened to emit a cry, a tear of passion, so destiny was consummated!') It is my belief that he contemplates her from a distance without even thinking of approaching her, addressing her... The withholding of his mother's affection, the careful repression of boarding-school, his withdrawn and brooding temperament make him awkward beyond all reasonable measure in his relations with girls, quite unable to deal with them; this is his main weakness and this is probably also the reason why his school-mates 'jeer' at him... The rest is common knowledge and is a logical consequence of his incompatibility with that ambience. He takes time off, wanders around instead of attending lessons; he doesn't devote himself much to his studies, and the Masters (the Characters) slate him with the following marks: 5 in Italian, 4 in Latin, 4 in Greek, 6 in history, 5 in philosophy, 6 in mathematics, 6 in physics, 6 in natural history.

Women: how to get on with women...A problem that finds no solution in the life of Dino Campana. Federico Ravagli writes about Dino as he knew him, a twenty-seven-year-old student at Bologna University: 'Judging him in our company, he appeared a misogynist. He never had a word or a glance for Dora or Irma or Nella or any of the girls behind the bar, though they chattered amicably at his set frown. He seemed indifferent and annoyed when the young men inside exclaimed with enthusiasm and lewd praise at some curvaceous female going past in the street.' And Mario Bejor, who met Dino in 1911 and continued to see him off and on until 1916, goes as far as to question his virility, asking: 'How much of the female spirit and sensibility – despite himself – did he have, that it should cause him such revulsion?'

From a certain stage in his life – roughly around the age of twenty-seven – Dino identifies sex with 'the bloated old whores leavened with sperm', with the 'colossal prostitutes' and the 'Mothers' lined up on the Genoa waterfront. In their wombs, his 'ancient fatherland', man approaches the 'great nothingness' of the times which preceded his birth and which will follow his death. The young and beautiful women – like the *liceo* girl Francesca, the creole Manuelita and others whose traces are to be found in his writings – really belong to the world of fantasy, they are creatures of fantasy. In the real, everyday world the poet, like other men, is attracted to them; but he knows and wishes to know nothing beyond the contemplation of their beauty... Here's one story. In 1916, in Leghorn, Dino manages to court a splendid young woman, the guest of the painter Bianca Fabroni Minucci from Marradi, without her being aware of it. 'He communicated by reciting poems,' the interested party relates many years later. 'But my head was full of other things: I was just about to leave for the front as a nurse and had lost my fiancé in the fighting... So I never realized that in reciting his poems Dino Campana was showing that he liked me. Bianca pointed it out to me. But as I've just said, my thoughts were elsewhere...'

Likewise, when Sibilla Aleramo first approaches him, Dino is surprised and at a loss, though he is now aged thirty-one. He turns to the literary critic Cecchi: 'Sibilla wrote to me: what's she after? I sent her an evasive reply.' He masks his fear by making up the most far-fetched tales: 'You know I left university on account of the female students, and the business isn't over yet.' He fibs like a child in order to assume a masculine credibility and experience which he does not possess: but he is not a good liar. 'The incredible Russian woman who's come from Africa' whom he uses to try to rouse Aleramo's jealousy is one Anna, a resident of Scarperia near Florence, but she is above all a figure in the *Canti Orfici*, she is 'la Russa' who goes down the street 'carrying the blossom and the weal of her lips' on her pallid face. And 'la Russa' in the *Canti Orfici* is the longed-for image of a variety girl whom the writer Alberto Viviani mentions among the habitués of the Florentine literary café Giubbe Rosse in the days of *Lacerba* magazine, that is, in 1913: 'A young woman from Russian Georgia, surnamed Nino, a marvel, but always high on champagne.' Among other things, she was credited with dancing on the tables and giving ravishing strip-shows...

June 1901. Dino's examination failure brings things to a head in the Campana household. His father is beside himself because he's found out about his son's absenteeism during his last few months at school and would like to know the reason why: 'What were you up to? Who were you with?' Dino: 'I wandered around... Alone.' His father: 'But why? Why?' A long silence. His mother: 'I've always told you he's mad. That this Campana family of yours is riddled.' In the end, the school-teacher Giovanni takes his decision: he'll take his son to Faenza for a psychiatric examination. 'If he is mad, he goes into the asylum.' Fortunately, the chosen doctor (a certain Alberigo Testi) gives sage advice: to wait until Dino has reached full physical maturity before formulating a diagnosis and prescribing treatment; not to exaggerate the significance of a poor performance at school, not to torment the lad, who, he says, is going through a delicate phase of 'psychic adjustment'. So as to get away from home, Dino goes to stay for a few weeks at the house of some relatives at Premilcuore and, on returning home in July, he manages to communicate with his father, either on his own or through his Uncle Torquato: explaining why he won't set foot in the Faenza *liceo* again. ('They'd made a butt of me.') He engages to study on his own, at home, to make up the year; he wants trust and understanding, and one may say that is what he gets. Educational experts are consulted, including one Solenni (?) from Florence, who advises that he take the entrance examination for the *liceo* third year at the Royal M. D'Azeglio Ginnasio-Liceo in Turin. Why? No answer can be given. Information dries up. In September 1902 Dino travels to Turin with his father, passes the examination and then goes to Carmagnola, a small town in Piedmont, about thirty kilometres from Turin, enters the local *Convitto* (State boarding-school) and follows the final year of *liceo* there as a boarder. His school reports (four of them: one every two months) suggest a clever and receptive pupil with inclinations and approaches of his own; not particularly drawn towards *belles lettres*, even struggling a little in written Italian (his first report shows a mark of 4; his last, 5). He obviously does not get on with his philosophy master, who gives him 3 for progress and 5 for conduct, and confirms his negative judgement (5) in the final report. The *maturità* public examination panel (whose names we know) for the summer examination session ending on 15 July 1903, fail or refer forty of the sixty-five candidates to the autumn session, and pass the remaining twenty-five. Among the latter is Campana Dino of Giovanni and Luti Francesca, born and resident in Marradi, with the following marks: 6 in Italian, 7 in Latin, 7 in Greek, 6 in geography and history, 7 in philosophy, 6 in mathematics, 7 in physics, 7 in natural history.

'In Italy I was arrested and spent a month in prison in Parma around 1902 or 1903.' So the 'insane' Campana says to the psychiatrist Pariani who interrogates him and whom he, in his delirium, considers 'an agent of the King of Italy' sent to enquire into his past so as to have him thrown out of the insane asylum, where he, in fact, is 'just fine'. (The results of the enquiry will eventually appear in print under the at best presumptuous title of *A Plain Life of the Writer Dino Campana*: a compendium of reticences, omissions, information which is never quite true and never quite false, imprecisions and errors.)

We know for a certainty that Dino was not in the Parma prison either in 1902 or in 1903 and that his name does not appear in the registers. Here in my suitcase is the copy of a document (sent to me by the writer Gino Gerola) dated 1 September 1950 and signed by the then-governor of the Parma prison, G. Jafrancesco. 'Subject: *Information on the poet Dino Campana.*' The communication, addressed to the Rovereto magistrate, reads: 'Please inform the university student Gino Gerola of Nosellara di Folgoria that a search through the registers and records of these penal establishments from the year 1891 until April 1913 and from 1900 until August 1950 has failed to discover any mention of the name of the poet Dino Campana.' Clear enough... If a person's name does not appear in a prison's records, the 'plain' logic would have it that the person in question never was there. Self-evidently. But since Dino Campana's story can be reconstructed only by taking into account the element of make-believe, of the imagination, which is implicit in it, well then, I shall try to go beyond what is self-evident, attempting to capture those elements of truth that are always present – beyond the veil of deception – in the 'insane' Campana's replies to his inquisitor Pariani. And I shall write down and try to prove what I am convinced of: that Dino was probably confined in Parma, in prison or some such place (in a police cell, for instance), but not in August 1902 or 1903. It was in the August of the following year...

In Florence, in August of 1903, Dino sits the entrance examination for the officer cadet course as laid down by Royal Decree No 429 of 26 November 1899 (*Regulations for military academies*). At the end of July, via the Marradi *Comune*, he sends an application on official stamped paper (one-lira denomination) and is summoned to Florence about three weeks later to take the 'tests' required by the *Regulations*: 'Written test in Italian: 5 hours. Written test in mathematics: 5 hours. Written test in history: 5 hours.'

On 2 November 1903 Dino registers at the University of Bologna, in the faculty of science, for the degree course in chemistry. Why? Evidently the information that he has passed the entrance examination to the Military Academy (the above Decree stipulates: 'Candidates will be informed of their examination results by the Ministry via the same authority through which their application was forwarded') has not yet reached the Marradi *Comune*, and schoolmaster Campana is unwilling to run the risk that his son, in case of failure, might sit idle until the following autumn. Registering at the University for the academic year 1903-04 is therefore a last-minute move sagely carried out pending the results of the tests from the military authority. The choice of subject – chemistry – is Uncle Torquato's, who, being the pharmacist's friend, envies his easy profits. But it is made with the nephew's consent. ('Just any old thing,' Dino will say later in Bologna, when asked why). And who can tell whether the fruits of his studies would have turned out

any different if he had entered one of the humanities faculties
... Personally, I doubt it, just as the party concerned
doubted it. (Ravagli: ' "You've chosen the wrong faculty,"
he was told; "you should have read literature." And Campana: "Literature? Maybe..." '.) When he puts himself
down to do chemistry Dino does not yet know he's a poet,
he merely senses something underlying all his daydreaming:
a sky thronged with stars that hint at 'the infinity of deaths',
the presence of an 'insatiate chimera', 'queen of melody'
and 'the world's soul'. . . (But what has literature to do with
that? Or chemistry?)

In December 1903 Dino spends three weeks in Modena for the induction which is the second phase in the selection of the cadets: three weeks of aptitude tests, marches, night reveilles, horsemanship, gymnastics. Enclosed within the Ducal Palace, the Academy is a self-contained world, a perfect mechanism that fascinates him from the moment he arrives. In the background, barely glimpsed, is a silent and foggy town with which the military school seems totally unconnected except for the stuccoed and mirrored Caffè Molinari, the only one the cadets are allowed to enter. On Christmas Eve Dino comes back to Marradi with the news that he's been accepted, that he'll be wearing uniform and following the first-year course. A Campana family reunion is held to fête the future *condottiero*; even the Mad Uncle joins in. (Fanny shuts herself away in her room with migraine.) When the table is cleared, Torquato calls the toast, saying: 'This lad, whose first steps in life we have followed with trepidation, is now on the point of leaving us, to join a family very much greater than ours, to which we bow our heads. Let his future be as resplendent as that of our new Italy, of which all of us gathered here wish him to be a protagonist!' (Applause). But when the guests have gone, the talk is about money: for the Academy is all very well, but it's expensive. The *Regulations for military academies*, under the heading 'Annual fee and charge for first outfit', state: 'The annual fee is 900 lire and is to be paid quarterly in advance on 1 October, 1 January, 1 April and 1 July. –

New entrants who join the school during the first fortnight of the month will pay for the entire month; those who join during the second fortnight will pay only for that fortnight. – Upon admission, a further sum of 350 lire for outfit is also to be paid. Cadets entering from military schools will be exempt from the outfitting charge. – Apart from fees and the outfitting charge, every cadet will pay, quarterly in advance, 120 lire per annum for replacement and repair of clothing and outfit in general and the provision of text-books and stationery.' Naturally, the schoolmaster has applied to pay half fees 'in consideration of family merits', he, Giovanni Campana, being 'in State employ, nominated by royal decree to the public service with right of pension'; but the grant cannot be counted on, and certainly not with immediate effect. It is conceded, say the regulations, 'within the limits of the funds allocated for that purpose year by year, giving priority to those most in need.' In a word: the fees must be paid. While Dino's mother wanders round the house in her shawl, reciting the rosary, and while Manlio pores over his accountancy books, the schoolmaster Campana talks to his son of sums and morality. 'This year,' he says, 'what with the Military Academy and the University, you're costing me at least fifteen hundred lire. We're not rich, as you know, we can't throw money away; we're paying to set you up, so that you can go your own way. You're grown up now, you're a man.'

In Modena, Dino Campana has nothing on his mind: he hasn't the time. 'Fitting in at Modena wasn't easy. Strict discipline. Always in a rush without stopping except to eat, and to sleep. *Seniors* treating *bighats* [freshmen] like doormats. Very strict instructors. So much gymnastics that you never recovered between one bout and the next. Plus exercises in horsemanship, with plenty of whip, the horses going mad amid the cursing and the outbursts of crude invective. "Legs down, you look like a cow," was the politest cry. Some of the cadets couldn't take it. They'd remove their stars and head for home with head hanging down. Most of them went through their breaking-in with gritted teeth.' These are the words of Nuto Revelli, another writer who passed through the Modena Academy, and they refer to the Thirties: but they just as perfectly fit the beginning of the century. And Revelli's text supplies that valuable detail about *bighats* (*cappelloni*) and *seniors*, which helps us to understand a poem of Dino's in which the *ciane* (tarts) call him a *bighat*, 'bighat poet'... Pier Paolo Pasolini, who understood not a thing about Campana, found that detail heart-melting. He found it strange and admirable to have invented, fifty years ahead of time, an expression which was destined to become current and popular in the Sixties, though in a slightly different version – *capellone* (*longhair*). But in Dino's time – and probably still today – *cappelloni* in Modena meant first-year officer cadets. And the 'bighat poet' is not the rebel poet but the freshman poet, the new boy among the poets...

More from Revelli: 'Once a week, a long bicycle run right up to the Apennines, pedalling even downhill on account of the solid tyres. Plenty of book-learning, from *synopses* which were almost as ancient as the Ducal Palace in which we lived. Not a very scintillating life: fifty minutes' – not a minute longer – furlough every evening. Meals were on the light side. Everything was done to bugle-calls – chewing, swallowing, digesting.'

Certainly, life at the military Academy is hard. But Dino stays on, he doesn't give in. He remains in Modena until the end of the first year of his course, and that tells us at least one thing: that he's not at odds with his surroundings, as he was at the Faenza *liceo*. It means that he throws himself into the exercise of such martial arts as gymnastics, horsemanship and fencing as well as into studies which include German language. Possibly he does less well in military subjects (military literature, warfare, the history of the art of war); but who can tell? The one certain fact is that at the end of that first year the Academy closes its doors to Dino, who has 'not passed the examination for the rank of sergeant': and here there are two possible hypotheses. The first, 'plain', hypothesis is that Dino fails to attain an overall mark for the year of 11/20, as required by the previously quoted *Regulations*, and that he is pronounced 'unsuited' to military life. The second, 'imaginative', hypothesis is that Dino fails the examination because he has not attempted it. That, on the eve of the examination something happens to him which is so serious as to bring about, in effect, his expulsion from the course...

Following up this imaginative hypothesis, before coming to Marradi I went to Modena to see where stood, at the beginning of this century, that worthy post-Unification institution which our fathers and grandfathers referred to as the *casino* – the house of pleasure. I had taken it into my head, why I don't know, that Dino's expulsion from the Academy had something to do with an ill-managed attempt at initiation into manhood; and that an echo of the incident was to be found in the *Fascicolo marradese* (Marradi Brochure) published by Ravagli, which mentions 'Ophelia's corpse' suddenly appearing to the poet at the end of an alley in the Bologna winter: to remind him of a far-off past and a long period of misery. 'I plunge down an alley and from the shadows a white shadow steps in front of me. Have you ever punched a night-whore at the bottom of an alley shouting: why why from the shadows do you want to appear to me as (show me) Ophelia's vile corpse?' 'And I punch her.'

The incident, cropping up insistently later in the *Canti Orfici* in three or four variants which I won't transcribe, turns into an invocation to Satan, almost a quotation from Baudelaire: 'O Satan, you who place the night-whores at the crossroads; you, who from the shadows show Ophelia's vile corpse; O Satan, take pity on my long misery!' But the first version contains a typical *casino*-scene of initiation into manhood, as I am assured by reliable people, once regular visitors at such establishments. It was fairly normal at the beginning of the century and still into the Thirties and Forties – the experts say – for a well-brought-up and long repressed young man to lose his self-control the first time he was taken to the *casino*: he would stammer, tremble, burst out shouting. If, with his initiation in view, he'd also filled himself with wine and liquor, the young man might well 'punch night-whores' and accomplish other suchlike exploits. In such cases, the police intervened. The *buon costume* (public morals) police squad, whose duty it was to keep the *casini* under surveillance, would arrest the rowdy, throw him into a cell or strong-room, and keep him locked in until he sobered up: and that was generally where the matter ended. The wild nights of young men of good family left no trace in the prison records except in the exceedingly rare cases which led to brawls involving injury or murder.

Wine... In Modena and elsewhere in Italy at the beginning of the century, wine was sold and drunk 'by the hour' in a kind of epic challenge between bibber and landlord which represented an all too shortlived economic model: over against free market exchange and the socialist economic order, a third path for the world economy. The drinker entered the inn, paid for an hour's drinking in advance, and poured as much wine down his throat as he could manage in an hour. Usually, he collapsed (just outside the city walls at Modena was a drinking-house known as 'The Electric Chair' because of the number of patrons who, having sat down there, proved unable to rise again unaided): but landlords sometimes went bankrupt too. Not far from 'The Electric Chair', between Via Armaroli and Via Catecumeno (two side-streets which are no longer to be found: they have been replaced by a piazza) were the old *casini*: and the Modenese who still remember those places said, yes, they might indeed fit Dino's account, given his 'alley' and his 'crossroads'... 'But,' they added immediately, 'a cadet from the Academy would never have dared venture down those alleys, not even by night, and not even in civvies.' 'As the Americans put it during the last war: *off-limits*, the area was out of bounds...', 'The entire district was *off limits.*' So I recollected Parma, and I mused: what if Dino's initiation into manhood was accomplished (or rather: unaccomplished) in Parma?

Certainly, Dino Campana experiences prison before he is twenty. He mentions it in a piece written in 1916: 'At eighteen years of age with the prison door shut upon me I cried out, weeping: Ideal government, you've pitched out numbers, such numbers of moral rabble.' His imprisonment may well have taken place in Parma, at the end of July 1904, and may have lasted a day rather than a month. Why not? Discussing his life with Pariani, Dino resorted precisely to the dodge of blowing up months into years and days into months, to shorten the interrogation...

Let us imagine the way things may have gone. Let's say: the day before the examination the cadets are allowed special leave to dine out with their families or see their sweethearts. One eye is shut even if they stay out all night, as long as they answer roll-call the following morning. Dino has made his plans, prepared and concerted in detail with a Parma comrade (whose name we do not know). They take the train to Parma: they change clothes in the Parma cadet's house, dine out, and when they've eaten enough tagliatelle and drunk enough lambrusco, they go questing for a nocturnal adventure in Parma. They smoke cigars, drink the walnut liqueur, *nocino*, and...go after women. (Given the period and the circumstances, the outcome is inevitable.) Unaccustomed to smoking and drinking, cadet Campana follows the cadet from Parma as in a dream: he sees the alley, the steps, the light, Ophelia's vile corpse. 'And I punch her.' Uproar. Two of the town guard seize Dino.

He struggles. The Parma cadet gets away. Next morning at roll-call cadet Campana is absent without leave and remains absent until evening, when he presents himself before the Academy commandant under guard by the 'public morals squad' from Parma who explain what has happened and take their leave. Without so much as a glance at the unlucky youth before him, the commandant orders him to be stripped of his arms, that is, his cadet's short sword, and confined to a cell. Three or four days, among the worst in the poet's life, go by: the rest of his class are sitting their examinations, and he... At last, on 4 August, he is sent for by the academic office, where a captain explains what a favour is being done to him in saving him the disgrace of being officially degraded and publicly expelled. 'In view of your not unbecoming behaviour up to this point, and since the authorities responsible for public order are not pursuing the matter... the General Commandant has decided to act magnanimously towards you by conceding something you do not deserve: a good conduct certificate.' He signs the paper before him, passes it to Dino: 'It goes without saying that you are not suited to continue the course and that you have not passes the examination for the rank of sergeant.' 'Like the French King François I at the battle of Pavia, all you preserve is honour and life to leave this place.'

It is not hard to imagine the state Dino is in on his way back to Marradi; nor is it difficult to picture the attitude of his family, his father's scorn and dismay, his mother's expostulations. The Campana household now enters upon its most violent period of conflict. It lasts six years and it will not be until 1910 that it tends to abate in frequency and intensity. After three attempts to get rid of their son (twice sending him to an insane asylum and once abroad), Fanny and Giovanni resign themselves to maintaining him, clothing him, seeing him around the house: and what is curious is this business of his parents resigning themselves – as if it were something natural – to care for their son at thirty after having sent him away in his youth. In the summer of 1904 there are furious rows: on the one side, reproaches for Dino's failures, his unruliness, the disgrace to the family, everything a nineteen-year-old lad can be reproached with; on the other side, a reaction of 'brutal, morbid impulsiveness'. Doors slammed, expletives, dishes and glasses sailing out through the window to land in the courtyard below. His mother always in the thick of the fray. ('Why did a woman call me a punk when I'd already been spat all over?') She won't put up with her son without first having broken him in. But it would be wrong to underestimate the role of the father, that schoolmaster Campana, 'a most upright man' – in the memory of the Marradians – 'and severe, one who made no concessions to sentiment.' He, though not persecuting his son as his wife Fanny does, certainly makes little effort to understand him and cannot bring himself to forgive him for having muffed his military career. His standpoint in family quarrels is clear and follows the principle that a gentleman may perhaps not see eye to eye with his children but cannot set himself against his spouse. (Decorum, first and foremost!) Then there's the matter of heredity, the disgrace of the Madman in the family, which is probably settled at this very period by his definitive removal to an asylum. This is carried out by the public authorities under orders from the mayor, as decreed by the brand-new law of 14 February 1904. In any case, what is the point of his staying in Marradi? Dino has not got through his exams at the Military Academy and who knows whether he'll ever be up to anything in life, 'unruly', and perhaps insane, as he is. Manlio is steady enough, poor fellow, but with not much of a head for book-learning. A blot on the family escutcheon won't prevent him from taking up book-keeping or getting a job in a bank. Torquato only has a daughter: her destiny, like that of any woman, is to live and work at home... If Francesco wants the Madman to keep his freedom, then it's up to him to take him into his house in Florence: here in Marradi we've had enough. (That is schoolmaster Campana's way of thinking and that is how, from one day to the next, the Madman's destiny is decided: he goes off to die in the madhouse, as the 'information sheet' records.)

The landscape around Marradi and the upper valley of the Lamone are dominated to the north by that ancient castle described in a prose passage of the *Canti Orfici* as being suspended between heaven and earth ('the highest and most distant castle'). Below the castle is Biforco, an outlying hamlet of Marradi. As the name indicates, this is where the road bifurcates, one branch leading to Campigno: a mule-track recently promoted to a motor-road thanks to a thin coating of asphalt spread over the stones. Campigno – not to be confused with Campigna, another of Campana's places, which stands opposite Mount Falterona – is a special sort of geographical entity and, for those within it, a total ambience. Everything is Campigno: the torrent, the valley, the village set in the valley. But as you go along the road you realize that there is no village, only houses: one house before the torrent, another house beyond it; one house on the mountainside, another below the road. I ask a woman hanging out her sheets in the meadow: where's Campigno? She raises an arm in a circular gesture: 'It's here. It's everything you can see.'

My eyes seek out the 'crags' where 'the hawk permanently resides.' It's an unassuming landscape. The mountains, seven or eight hundred metres high, are clad in wooded scrub – broom, hornbeam, beech, occasional chestnut trees. Where the rock is visible it's as though the mantle of woodland had been ripped, letting the nakedness show through. Of hawks, not a sign. Who knows what these places were like eighty years ago; who knows what they looked like to Dino? For he used to come up here very frequently to read, to study, to get away from the household. To locate his memories 'in Tuscany's landscape': to contemplate, by night, 'the stars' magnetic glare'.

At Campigno, at the beginning of the century, everybody knows the Campanas. Dino comes here with relatives while he's still in short pants, and the Campignesi call him 'the young gentleman', 'the young master'. (Reserved, and slightly surly, Giovanni barely manages to greet these hill-folk who bow to him or, if they see him from a distance, doff their caps. The more communicative Torquato enters the ploughmen's houses, enquires into the ups and downs of the occupants' health, into the latest births, both to humans and livestock, drinks a glass of wine and offers a cigar in return, gives playful cuffs to the children and kicks to the dogs and leaves to a chorus of blessings and farewells.) But it is only from the summer of 1904 that 'the young master' becomes a regular visitor to the valley: he secludes himself behind the hedges, remains motionless there for hours, book in hand, and by this behaviour soon perturbs the poor Campignesi, who find him odd and misguided... ('Who ever heard of a young lad of nineteen, in good health and comfortably off, who could be chasing all the girls in the valley, coming to skulk up on the mountains like a beast?' 'You mark my words, that fellow's crazy. All that study's turned him peculiar.' 'He'll finish the same way as his uncle.') It's here, just outside Marradi, that the 'raving' apprentice's earliest 'urges for a wandering life' appear; and it's here that someone from Marradi takes to tapping his forehead upon seeing him walking along with two or three books under his arm...

Another of Dino's walks follows the road from the outskirts of Marradi to San Benedetto in Alpe. The landscape here, unlike that around Campigno, is picturesque from the first; the vegetation is varied. Pines, cypresses and upland pastures alternate along the valleys with stretches of Mediterranean scrubland or thistles. The road verges, the meadows, the rock-crannies are dotted with flax flowers: flax crops were cultivated, at the beginning of this century, in little sky-blue fields just behind the houses. Where the mountain flanks are more bare and rugged, the rocks, in stratum upon stratum, speak of remote eras, of long-vanished seas, of plains that have been turned into mountains by that collision of continents that knows no pause, that is in progress now . . . And you still encounter sights which take you back to the poet's lifetime: the shepherd-girl standing at the road's edge, the donkey laden with brushwood. Beyond the Hermit's Pass (Passo dell' Eremo), at an altitude of 921 metres, I find the road in turmoil with tracked vehicles ripping and slicing a way through the mountain so as to lay a huge pipe. Exchanging yells, amid that implausible din, I learn that it's a methane pipeline . . .

Dino used to pass this way when visiting relatives at Premilcuore or when venturing out far from Marradi on one of those walks of his that might last up to two or three weeks. He would go as far as Castagno d'Andrea, Campigna, Falterona. Only amid these mountains did he feel 'at home': and the only accurate note in the epigraph which his Uncle Torquato dictated to him in 1928 is precisely the mention of the Mugello highlands in 'Tuscan Romagna'. 'Dino Campana,' reads the epigraph, 'was born on 20 August 1885 in Marradi, which is also the home of Professor Federico Ravagli, known particularly in Germany and America for his scholarly researches.

Afflicted at fifteen years of age by confusion of spirit, he subsequently committed errors of every kind, each of which he atoned for with great suffering.

He retained his honour, though it now no longer served him, and, in witness to himself, at various stages of his wandering life, wrote this book.

He was last heard of from the mountains of Tuscan Romagna.'

'Afflicted at fifteen years of age by confusion...' Poor Dino Campana, or rather, poor Dino Edison: already ravaged by the disease which infected his blood in Genoa in 1912 and by 'electrical stimuli', as the psychiatrist Pariani demurely terms them. ('My name is Dino Edison.' 'I'm electric.') It was even his lot to write his own epigraph... It so happens that after Torquato's death the family find among his papers in Marradi this strange autograph of the poet's: they send it to Falqui and Falqui publishes it as 'a most worthy leave-taking from an existence overcrowded with tribulations but conscious of leaving poetic witness to itself, its sufferings, its joys, in self-clarification.' No one even remotely suspects that the document contains nothing of Dino's but his hand-writing, and that the wisdom and the self-awareness belong to the man of letters, Torquato (along with the admiration for the scholarly Ravagli, 'known particularly in Germany and America', and Marradi's roll of honour, and the convic-tion that his nephew's insanity began 'at fifteen years of age', and the blazon of Dino's 'honour' which 'now no longer served him' but nevertheless still exists...). No one, in a word, suspects that it is a forgery, carried out with good intent but rather crudely... Yet this is the only plaus-ible explanation. The 'auto-epigraph' published by Falqui, from which we are to infer that while in the asylum Dino took other people's viewpoint on himself and concerned himself with Marradi's local history, is an expression of the scruples which assail poor Torquato, probably in 1928, after he has made over to Vallecchi the rights to the work of the 'insane' poet. What if – Torquato muses – the publisher is merely seeking to make money out of Dino's misfortunes? What if Vallecchi is trying to fabricate a phoney and dishonourable literary scoop, based not so much on the poetry as on the poet's personal mishaps and misdemeanours? (Perhaps he's read the preface by Binazzi; perhaps his suspicions have arisen spontaneously.) At length he devises a solution: he'll take the publisher a note in his nephew's own hand for insertion into the book: a message from the madhouse, summarizing and vindicating his vexed but stainless existence... But Vallecchi's response is totally discouraging: 'The man's obituary – minus the mention of Ravagli – might perhaps serve as an inscription on his tombstone. It won't do for the book. Let's forget about it.' Or else Torquato himself, after having dictated the epigraph, decides against using it – who can tell. Only two things are certain. First, that the epigraph has survived, to the edification of posterity and to the perpetuation of the memory of this Ravagli (the third person by that name in the life-history of the poet). Second, that it is in Dino's own hand...

Returning to 1904-1905, we know that Dino spends a great deal of time in the mountains around Marradi; that he reads; that he plays the piano and – as he himself is later to tell Pariani – that he 'writes'. (Probably reflections, observations, notes on his readings: not poetry as yet.) 'I wrote some critical articles,' says Dino, 'on new books, books of poems. Impressions; they haven't been reprinted. The earliest? – I'd have been about twenty.' If we substitute the simple for the iterative form of the verb ('they haven't been printed'), we have a reliable fact: for there is indeed no evidence that Dino Campana ever published any articles of literary criticism. While it is probable – altogether likely, I would say – that at the age of twenty he pores and ponders over the books he reads, or at least some of them, that he debates with himself over them and writes notes and even tries to translate them, if they are in foreign languages. During the war years Dino will entrust to a relative of his in Cignato, which is another district in the Marradi area, 'a large soap-box, crammed with manuscripts', which – as testified by Bejor – will be used as firelighters: 'The whole lot was burnt, down to the last sheet.'

'Art, awesome one!, still / you have not unveiled yourself. / We worshipped you in vain. // Glory, you pass by, and to other / brows award your kiss. // We followed you in vain. // Unknown beloved, ah, too, / too young you died. / We waited for you in vain.' – These lines, among the best known of D'Annunzio's at the beginning of the century, must have counted for something in Dino's life: if it is true – as I believe it is – that until the summer of 1905 he remains incredulous and almost awestruck at the thought of being a poet. A poet, the books tell him, is greater and less than a man. He is the tangible representation of the survival of thought ('Before us in the dark, / Death holds no torch. / – Glory! – We shall die in vain') and of art. As for poetry... Dino knows from D'Annunzio that poetry is a terrible gift and an absolute wager; from Carducci, he knows it to be a tough apprenticeship, a craft. His own personal meditations, his readings, his school-teachers and even (why not?) the discipline of the Military Academy: all conspire towards the slow maturation in the mind of the young Campana of an idea of art as something arduous and aristocratic; that same idea which will, in later years, lead him to reject membership of any literary circle ('Everything is individual effort') and to deliver sharp and unkind judgements on his contemporaries. (On Soffici: '*Un paysan qui aurait lu Baudelaire.*' On Papini: 'The market-place charlatan of poetry.' On Prezzolini and his followers of the *La Voce* [The Voice] group: 'The *vociani*: *voci* [voices] + *ani* [anuses].' On the Futurists: 'They want to give birth to a new art just by squelchings.') The idea that will lead him to regard the *littérateurs* of his time as dilettantes without any firm grounding and without serious aspirations; and to accuse them of taking their stones from the edifice of the Italian artistic tradition and of being mere *parvenus* and pilferers... ('A generation of pilferers is entering the world of letters.' 'The Italian people sing no more.' 'Oh, *parvenu*! You are our ruin.')

'I read a lot here and there,' Campana will tell Pariani. 'I liked Carducci a lot; Pascoli, D'Annunzio. Poe, too; I read a lot of Poe. Among musicians I greatly admired Beethoven, Mozart, Schumann. I like Verdi, too; Spontini, Rossini. Ha! I know all these; they were always playing Italian music in Argentina.' But these are vague indications. Carducci and D'Annunzio and Nietzsche are certainly among the authors that Dino ponders over and writes notes on in the Campigno mountains. And Pascoli, echoes of whom can be detected in some of his juvenile poems. The reference to wide and undisciplined reading, much richer than this brief avowal reveals ('I read a lot here and there') is highly plausible. As to his musical interests, there are only these other bare pointers by Dino: 'I wanted to study chemistry, but then I gave up studying because it didn't suit me; I took up studying the piano.' 'I wrote a bit, studied the piano a bit.'

Having failed the officers' course, Dino is left with chemistry ('black cataloguing science'): poring over books and in laboratories, graduating, finding employment in a pharmacy making up powders for the rest of his days. Dino promises: he'll study. Between one scene and the next (his mother accusing him of being a loafer, a scrounger, a vagrant, a good-for-nothing; of setting the family on the road to ruin and tarnishing its reputation by his madman's escapades; 'you lunatic! you failure!' she yells), his future is settled. He'll go and live at his uncle Francesco's in Florence; he'll register at Florence University. An outfit is put together for him (some linen, underwear, some breeches and 'reversed' jackets of his father's); a pair of shoes is purchased and an oval wicker suitcase, the same that will accompany him to Argentina and to Castel Pulci, everywhere. (Bianca Luseno, Livorno 1916: 'His entire luggage consisted of an oval wicker suitcase, more like a basket than a suitcase. In it he kept a few clothes, books, in particular several copies of the *Canti Orfici*... and a black scarf, even in summer...') On 20 December 1904 Dino obtains a transfer from the University of Bologna to the Istituto Superiore in Florence and from pure to pharmaceutical chemistry. He is in Florence by early January and the city appeals to him at once with its history, its monuments, its severe, composed spaces where for the first time he 'feels' one can be a poet while remaining just an ordinary man in the street and wearing ordinary clothes like everyone else. It's a dazzlingly simple idea. Florence, 'nest of creeps', a town peopled by 'a mass of lick-spittles, pansies, flunkeys, cracked bards, tumblers, journalists and philosophers', still remains one of the spots on this earth where it is possible to 'put some body into one's imaginings'. As he is to write subsequently to Papini: 'But if you have any need at all to create, don't you feel rising all around you the primordial energy with which to put some body into your imaginings?'

University, chemistry... Urged on by his uncle, Dino follows his course but does not get to grips with it, doesn't manage to concentrate on the words he is listening to, the formulas chalked up on the blackboard. Contemplating his female fellow-students suggests chords and images which are poetic tesserae. ('Her bowed, ivory brow, flashing,' 'In the circle of her sinuous lips.' 'Enchanting dusky-rose girl.') He wanders from the chemistry lecture-halls to the halls of letters without finding different or greater stimuli. He steps outside. He mingles with the passers-by in Via Cavour, Via dei Servi; he looks at the new books displayed in the booksellers' windows: D'Annunzio, Pascoli (the Hellenistic twilight of the *Poemi Conviviali*), Bertacchi's now forgotten *Malíe del passato* [Enchantments of the Past], Grazia Deledda's *Cenere* [Ash], Ugo Ojetti's *Il cavallo di Troia* [The Trojan Horse], the latest issue of the little magazine *Il Leonardo*. He goes along Via Calzaiuoli towards Piazza della Signoria; he enters the Uffizi gallery and wanders through its corridors and halls or else proceeds over the Ponte Vecchio towards the Boboli gardens and climbs up to Piazzale Michelangelo... In Via Santo Spirito, at his uncle's house, they might wait for him in vain at lunchtime and when, in the evening, they ask where he's been, Dino shrugs vaguely: 'Nowhere in particular... Just to look at the paintings in the Uffizi.' 'A little stroll round Florence...'

Springtime excites Dino like coffee – at twenty, his only 'vice'. His walks extend as far as Settignano, the village in the hills towards Fiesole. Possibly he encounters one day a horseman accompanied by two greyhounds and recognizes him as Gabriele D'Annunzio, but that encounter – if it occurs – leaves no trace of memory. In fact by the spring of 1905, Dino Campana's youthful infatuation with D'Annunzio (idol of two whole generations, Dino's and the one following) has already waned; even the D'Annunzian Sibilla Aleramo, who eleven years later declaims D'Annunzio's *Laudi* to the night, will not succeed in resuscitating it. ('Why did we read D'Annunzio before we left?' Dino asks her in a letter. 'No one ages a woman or a landscape as he does.') He is elated by the Florentine gardens and the light of Tuscany. He's elated by the springtime and the way the girls of Florence carry themselves: 'From the way they walk you can tell the earth exists to hold them up.' Chemistry and the University are forgotten completely, so that the *avvocato* Francesco Campana writes to his brother informing him that his son seems to derive no benefit from studying chemistry, in which – says Francesco – he shows not the slightest interest. 'He mostly visits museums and, when he's at home, reads books: novels, poetry.' On the following Thursday – nearly all the exploits of school-master Campana fall on a Thursday, that being the primary schools' day off – Giovanni descends on Florence by the first train: it's May, almost the end of the academic year.

Dino is already out. His father hurries over to the University, secures an interview with the secretary of the science faculty: together, they check through the entries for the summer examinations. 'Nothing here,' says the secretary. 'And anyway,' he adds benevolently, 'in order to register for an examination a student must have a record of attendance and I have my doubts whether the young fellow... What did you say the name was? Ah, Campana. As I was saying, I have my doubts as to whether this son of yours has been attending any courses... Take my advice, since you're here: go over to the departments of physics and inorganic chemistry, which are the first-year subjects. Ask if anyone knows your son, whether he's been seen at the lectures...'

August 1905. After yet another row, Fanny goes to spend a few days with relations in Premilcuore and we seize the opportunity to conjure up a sort of family council, including Francesco, in Marradi, outlining the attitude of each of them towards Dino. His father opens: 'I no longer know what to think of my son. Believe me, I've tried everything. He seems reasonable enough to talk to, as you know: good-natured towards everyone except his mother; of above average intelligence; but there's something perverse about him that nullifies even his good qualities. What's to be done? You tell me. Should he be found a job, away from Marradi maybe, so as to oblige him to be self-sufficient? Should he be given one last chance to complete his studies? Should he be committed to an asylum for a period of treatment? For my part, I'm convinced that there's something wrong with him. He certainly can't stay here with us. His mother says: it's either him or me.'

'He's a confused young man,' says Francesco. 'Possibly he's to blame for everything that's happened to him so far, but one can't keep thwarting him and ignoring his inclinations. That's bound to drive him mad.' Giovanni: 'Alas, he's that already. If you could see the way he reacts when his mother corrects him... And then, you'd have to tell us, what *are* his inclinations? To stroll around? To write poetry?' Torquato: 'After all, he's only twenty. Of the two years he's wasted, he gained one by skipping the first year of *ginnasio*. So I say the situation can be saved and that he can complete his studies. Not in Florence, where he finds too many distractions, but in Bologna, under guidance.' Francesco: 'Now I'll tell you what I'd do if the lad were my own son. I'd take him out of University, where in any case he's not going to achieve anything, and I'd let him study music, art, acting, I'd ask him what *he* would like to go in for, and then I'd go along with his wishes.' 'Dino has artistic talent. Why force him into chemistry?' Giovanni and Torquato, simultaneously: 'He opted for it!' 'That was his doing!' Giovanni: 'Anyway, to me this art business is pie in the sky. He goes up the mountains, reads, jots down a few things, in Florence he goes wandering around instead of studying, at home he deafens his poor mother, who suffers from migraine, practising the piano. But to say that that means he has any sort of talent, Francesco...!) Torquato: 'No, no, Giovanni's right. It's just a juvenile delusion. Which of us three hasn't written a poem or two when he was twenty? Which of us hasn't dreamt of being some kind of artist?'

We know from family memoirs of a meeting between Dino and the grand old scholar-poet Giosuè Carducci during this same summer of 1905 or (less likely) of the following year. Carducci, ailing since 1899, has been in retirement since the end of 1904, when he gave up his Chair of Italian Literature at Bologna University, to be awarded a pension 'for especial merit' two months later, in January, by Act of Parliament. He is staying at the house of the obscure Counts Pasolini in Faenza and each morning walks the short distance to the 'barbarian tower' and the outdoor tables of the Caffè Centrale, where he lingers a few minutes beneath – no, 'beside' – the tower. ('To one side in vast lightning the tower, eight-cusped red impenetrable arid'.) Twenty-year-old Dino, light chestnut hair, straw-coloured thin moustache, for some unknown reason is staying in Faenza, along with his brother. He sees the Bard, Carducci, affably returning the greetings of Faenza people whom he doesn't know, with his characteristic, almost jerky, manner replying to their enquiries: 'How are you feeling, Maestro?' 'Will you be staying with us for a few days?' Dino stares at him, spellbound. ('Carducci has a German way of holding his head.') He approaches the poet, bows. – Not a word has come down to us of the brief dialogue that passes between them. But is there anything against our imagining that the old poet takes a liking to that young man with sincere eyes and an awkward manner? 'What's your birth, my lad?' 'Dino Campana. From Marradi. Studying chemistry.' Carducci's head gives a jerk. 'An alchemist... Sit here. Listen. "Now coal and iron are the fashion / Like hornets we all buzz around. / Absinthe gives us a fine reaction: / We cough our lungs out on the ground."' He pauses a moment, muses? 'I wrote those lines many long years ago, in a different century... How will this century turn out,' he wonders, 'of which I can only glimpse the first light of dawn?' 'The lines are very up-to-date,' ventures Dino. But the Bard's interest has flickered out. His hand makes a brief valedictory gesture. 'Our farewell is *a Dio*, go with God. But what I bid you, young alchemist, is to go with matter. Exalt it.'

In Marradi in 1905 Dino is not yet officially 'the village idiot', but he's on the way to it, thanks to the disinterested efforts of a number of people. These include the next-door neighbours, who listen in to the uproar between him and his mother. There are Fanny's church confidantes, and the marriageable girls who can't understand why 'the schoolmaster's son' doesn't show them all the attention they deserve. And the mountain-folk of Campigno, and the Mad Uncle's devotees, and Dino's own peers and former schoolmates... Each and every one does all that he or she can to rouse that monster, Rumour, *Fama*, about which Virgil in the *Aeneid* writes that she flies by night, 'squeaking in the shadow betwixt earth and sky'. 'I can still see him,' his ancient parish priest Pietro Poggiolini will say in the Fifties, 'being pointed to and labelled as mentally unbalanced! As a person who just hadn't grasped what ordinary living was all about. He'd go down to the Lamone, the river where he'd played as a boy, and heaven knows what ideas would come into his mind just then! Certainly, he wished he could talk to someone, but no one approached him. The children who usually play at the river's edge or on its dry bed would watch him; he would call them, but, instead of drawing closer, they would scoot off like hares... And he would stand there following them with his gaze, then, with a shake of his head, walk off along the embankment kicking the loose stones!'

Don Poggiolini's recollections are a telling record of the

initial phase of a hostility that, with the passing of time, is
to take on a violent character and turn into outright persecution. (Instead of scooting off, the children begin to taunt
the 'madman', throw stones at him, set matches between
his fingers when he's drunk and then light them; the adults
drive him out of public premises on the pretext of 'avoiding
trouble'.) Dino escapes more and more frequently into the
mountains, into that Campigno valley which is his Far
West, his Eldorado, and which, in the prose passages of the
Canti Orfici, becomes a magic spot, a mythological scenario:
'Campigno: barbaric landscape, elusive land of night, mystic incubus of chaos. Your folk's gestures conjure up the
night of the ancient human beast. Grotesques are silhouetted
in your heaving mountains: a lout, a crabbed whore rush
off under the racing clouds. And your banks white as
clouds, triangular, billowing sails: barbaric landscape, elusive land of night, mystic incubus of Chaos.'

'Squeaking in the shadow betwixt earth and sky...' – But before Rumour lays hold of him, for good and all, Dino assays one more attempt at normality, at making his peace with Marradi. He shuts himself up in his room (this is the summer of 1905) and spends months and months swotting up his first-year chemistry course, with determination, almost in despair, following his father's instructions, which are intended to enable him to make up for lost time and catch up with the examination schedule by October 1906. He studies mineralogy, botany, physics, inorganic chemistry. (University records show that Dino took these examinations, at Bologna, and give his marks, which I shall shortly divulge.) In order to obtain his attendance certificate, his father goes to see the faculty secretary and wins his sympathy with stories that have by now acquired truth in the telling. 'My son,' he tells him, 'has been suffering from a nervous affliction, and during the year he spent in Florence he was seized by a wanderlust that took him away from lectures, so that he's lost a year. Now he's studying on his own, he's bent on making up for lost time, and I believe he'll manage if he gets a helping hand, if the professors will give him their support.'

By early February, Dino is fully prepared in all subjects, he only has a few qualms about physics. The designated day arrives. The aspiring pharmacist leaves Marradi by train before daybreak and, after various vicissitudes, gets through his first examination (botany), inevitably with the minimum pass-mark of eighteen out of thirty. – Why 'in-evitably'? Simply because the Italian university institution at the beginning of the twentieth century follows regular behaviour-patterns which make it fairly easy to predict teacher-pupil relations. From the professorial point of view (speaking generally, of course, and ignoring single excep-tions to the norm), the pupil is merely a distraction holding up research: he gets in the way of consultancies, travel, business. He is a 'nuisance' who should be kept 'in his place' or, if possible, even further away. The professor robs the student of lecturing-time by 'academically' delaying the start of the lecture; wastes his time, money and effort through professorial whims in delaying or cancelling examinations on the most trifling pretexts; professorial sulks and tantrums involving dressing-downs or mockery, or the setting of hopelessly long or irrelevant assignments, remind the pupil that, to his professor, he is a nobody. What most inclines a Master to put up with a pupil is servil-ity and dog-like devotion on the latter's part: intellect and knowledge of his subject take second place, and indeed may be regarded with suspicion ('who does that fellow think he is?'). It is therefore unthinkable that an unknown pupil should present himself before the Master, without having attended lectures and undergone the statutory sufferings, for the supreme moment of examination, and obtain a decent mark... The professor has already performed a miracle in admitting him. He might consent to give him a pass if he shows himself a humble, diligent and pleasant lad: but only with the minimum mark!

The unknown pupil Campana, in February 1906, passes his botany exam and then takes mineralogy and inorganic chemistry without the slightest chance in the world of obtaining a mark higher than eighteen out of thirty, both on the grounds I have already given (that he hasn't been through his ordeal at the hands of the Masters) and because there is another academic custom by which the first mark given determines the next, almost mechanically, and nearly always to the student's detriment. (That is, successive marks may go down but may not go up.) So Dino's situation when he takes his fourth examination (physics) is such that, if his marksheet showed three previous marks above twenty, the professor would give him an eighteen, and he would be through. But as he has three eighteens, his professor enters a 'fifteen' on his record and hands it over to him with some ironic remark characteristic of the times. (Say, 'I'll give you the rest of the mark at the next session if you've done some work. Good day.')

'Mario Bejor (a close friend of Campana's between approximately 1911 and 1914) relates that the poet confided to him
that five years earlier, that is around 1907, in Bologna station
one day he was seized by a sudden desire to get away. With
only a small sum of money in his pocket, he slipped on
board the first northbound train and spent the entire journey
locked in the toilet...' So writes Gerola in his biography
of Campana. But the date is unreliable. Other things are
happening to Dino in 1907. His 'great escape' from his family, from Marradi, from University, from the unjust and
hypocritical society which oppresses him, takes place early
in 1906 and in all likelihood relates to his physics exam
result. From Via Zamboni, where the University is located,
Dino makes for the station through the heavy February fog.
His thoughts are as gloomy as the surrounding scenery.
'The unkind vapours of the fog sulk amid the buildings,
veiling the tops of the towers, the long streets silent and
deserted as if after pillage. Some girls, all of them small, all
of them dark, artfully wound in their mufflers, skip across
the streets, making them emptier still. And in the incubus
of fog, in that graveyard, they suddenly seem to me like so
many little animals, all alike, skipping along, all of them
black, going off to brood in lengthy hibernation over an
evil dream.'

He enters the station building, heads towards the trains.
'Along the railway track the goods-yard could be seen close
at hand in the false perspective of the leaden light... Dull

strokes, whistles from the goods-yard accentuated the monotony which suffused the air. The steam from the engines mingled with the fog: the wires strung themselves along from one bunch of campanulas to another on the telegraph posts that followed on behind one another automatically.'

He reads the timetable displaying departures for Rimini. And suddenly he realizes that he has no intention of returning to Marradi: that any destiny, for him, is preferable to the nightmare of that place and those people. (To his hysterical mother's yelling and convulsions; to his father's hollow and slightly ridiculous pomposity; to the incomprehension and hostility of the locals.) There and then, he decides: he'll get on a train, and be off. With nowhere to go, with no money, without regrets for anything he's leaving behind. But with one certainty: that even if everything goes wrong, things will be no worse than they have been. He walks over to a train that has just come in, and asks a railwayman: 'Where to?' The other fails to understand. 'Where to, what?' 'The train?' The man checks his watch. 'That's the Milan express, continuing to Switzerland.'

The 'great escape' takes place between the end of February of 1906 and 10 May of the same year (when schoolmaster Campana subjects his son to his second psychiatric examination). About what happened during those months Dino only gave veiled hints, as usual. He produced a sort of dissolving shot of it, in which memory turns into dream. 'Oh! I remember! I was young, my restless hand cupping my undecided face, tender with yearning and fatigue. So I proffered my enigma to smooth and sinuous seamstresses, hallowed by my yearning for the supreme love, the yearning of my boyhood, tormented and thirsting. All was mystery to my faith, my life was all one yearning for the secret of the stars, all one leaning over the abyss. I was comely with torment, restless pallid thirsting questing after the phantoms of mystery. Then I fled. I lost myself amid the din of the colossal cities, I beheld the white cathedrals soar into the sky, enormous medleys of faith and dream with their thousand pinnacles, I beheld the Alps soar even higher like still greater cathedrals, and filled with the great green shadows of the firs, and filled with the melody of the torrents whose singing I heard springing from the infinity of dream. Up there among the firs vaporous in the mist, among the thousand thousand clickings the thousand voices of silence unveiled a young light between their trunks, along paths of blue I rose: I rose up to the Alps, against a backdrop of white delicate mystery. Lakes, up there among the rocks, bright pools watched by the dream's smile, bright pools the ecstatic lakes of oblivion that you Leonardo imaged.'

So reads one of the prose *Canti Orfici*, 'La notte' [Night]. And it isn't hard to make out the sites of Dino's escape: Milan, the lakes and Switzerland . . . But the escape goes on. Other memories, other traces surface in other pieces of the *Canti Orfici* to complete the interrupted tale. In 'Dualismo (Lettera aperta a Manuelita Etchegarray)', for instance, Dino says he remembers Paris beneath the 'electric lamps' of the little library in Bahía Blanca: implying that he has been to Paris before going to Argentina. Or in 'Incontro di Regolo' (Meeting with Regolo), which speaks of a tramp – Regolo – whom Dino meets in South America in 1908 but whom he knows already, having met him in Italy 'on the road to Pavia', 'down at heel, his coat-collar pulled up around his ears'. Is it too much to hazard that Dino meets Regolo on the same day that he escapes from Bologna? That this personage is his first fellow-bohemian? (Two points suggest and support this hypothesis. First, the 'road to Pavia'; then the 'coat-collar pulled up around his ears': which refers us to the fog and frost of a February day . . .)

Locking yourself inside a train toilet is a dodge that doesn't get you very far. So Dino gets off at Piacenza, asks the way to Milan, crosses an extremely long bridge over a river which must be the Po, which *is* the Po: and immediately finds himself among the fields. (Where, then, was the town?) He walks through the fog for how long he cannot say – maybe an hour, maybe two – until he sees ahead of him a man going in the same direction, bowed under the weight of two enormous knapsacks: he draws up alongside him, addresses him. Just for company's sake. To hear the sound of his own voice. Before Italy turned into one vast motor-circuit, from the Alps to the farthest tip of Sicily, people actually spoke to one another. He asks the other whether he too is going to Milan, and offers to carry one of his knapsacks. 'I'm going to Pavia,' the man says. 'I branch off left at the next place.' He sets down his bags, introduces himself: 'Regolo Orlandelli, traveller.'

Regolo Orlandelli... Who knows whether this was the real name of Dino's *alter ego*? The surname appears only in Pariani's book, and Dino purposely gave Pariani vague and imprecise information. 'Regolo's a chap who went to Argentina. Regolo Orlandelli was his name, he was from Mantua. I met him in Argentina, in Bahia Blanca. Before that, I'd met him near Milan. He travelled the world. In America he had an employment agency: in Milan he was a tinker. In Genoa I ran into him after I'd been to Argentina. I think he's dead; he must have died, definitely.' The Argentinian writer Gabriel Cacho Millet has told me that he searched for traces of this Regolo Orlandelli on both sides of the ocean and found none: but that does not mean that Regolo is a fiction of Campana's. Indeed, I would rule out such a possibility on the grounds that – as far as I know, and until there is proof to the contrary – nothing in the *Canti Orfici* is completely fictitious. Even tiny details, even apparently insignificant ones, turn out to refer to something real, closely or remotely connected. To return to Regolo: possibly his name was Orlando Regolini rather than Regolo Orlandini; perhaps he didn't come from Mantua but from Rovigo; who can tell. And it may also be true that time has obliterated every trace of him, both in Argentina and in Italy. My enquiry into Dino Campana has taught me how hard it is to reconstruct the life of a man who has not been the object of history during his lifetime. Every recollection is lost within the space of a few years, a few decades at most; wars, and the unconcern of the living, destroy records, archives, documents. A bench or a carpet may last for centuries: not a man's memory. As the *Book* says: 'An infinite emptiness. An infinite nothing. All is empty nothing.'

The life of the vagabond Regolo recurs in Dino's life with surprising analogies, at least one of them prophetic. So let us open the *Canti Orfici* on the page which describes the last meeting between Dino and Regolo, in Genoa. Let us read in the *Canti Orfici* (printed, remember, in the summer of 1914) the portrait of Regolo who is paralysed, irritated, who keeps touching 'the motionless part' of his face and wants to go away, to get out...

'Clapped out several times, syphilitic in the end, a drinker, a wastrel, the demon of novelty in his heart shooting him into trying his luck, always successfully, that morning his sodden nerves had let him down and his right side had remained paralysed for a quarter of an hour, the cast in his eye staring at this phenomenon, while he kept touching the motionless part with his irritated hand. He'd recovered, he'd come to see me and wanted to get out.'

'But how could he get out? My quiet madness that day irritated him. His paralysis had embittered him. I watched him. The right side of his face was still numb and contracted and on his right cheek was the furrow of a tear but just a single, involuntary tear, which had rolled out of his staring eye: he wanted to get out.'

'I walked and walked amid the amorphous crowd of people. From time to time I could see his skewed eye staring at the phenomenon, at the motionless part that seemed to attract it irresistibly: I could see his irritated hand that kept touching the motionless part. Every phenomenon is in itself serene.'

Regolo Orlandini and Dino Campana part company 'in Piazza Corvetto' in Genova, definitively ('He left'): but their lives continue their parallel development towards an identical epilogue. In the summer of 1915 Dino too is visited by paralysis, and, with the paralysis, by the same disease which Regolo wanted to give the slip. And that disease is a sort of darkness which little by little clouds his intellect: something horrible, chill, nameless. 'Meanwhile I was at my wits' end in Florence on account of the beginnings of a vasomotory paralysis down my right side and those Florentines wouldn't admit me into hospital. Now I'm pulling through on my own. Let me tell you anyway that I was being treated for *nephritis*, whereas I had a cerebral congestion, for a month in the local hospital' (letter to Mario Novaro, 25 December 1915). '*Je suis maintenant un peu paralisé*' (letter to Giovanni Boine, 17 January 1916). 'I've been ill for seven months. I had a cerebral congestion; now I'm suffering from a slight weakening of the circulatory system down my right side. I'm still hoping for a recovery, though there are plenty of things interfering with it. Never mind' (letter to his brother, 1 April 1916). 'My health is as usual. Some swelling on my right side, and trembling. I've been at the hospital here for forty days, they fobbed me off by saying I had: *nephritis*!!' (letter to Emilio Cecchi, 28 March 1916). 'Writing is out, my nerves won't take it any more' (letter to Novaro, 12 April 1916: and it's worth taking the trouble to point out how in the twilight of Dino Campana's reason – which begins precisely in the autumn of 1915 – the first thing to be extinguished is poetry, Which, plainly, does not thrive on mental disorder...).

But, one may well say, what of that mysterious malady; what Dino calls 'cerebral congestion' and the Marradi hospital doctors call 'nephritis' and the psychiatrist Pariani regards as the initial phase of 'dissociative madness'? ('Sometimes attacks of this kind occur at the onset of dissociative madness.') Is it destined to remain mysterious, or do its symptoms tally with something known and named? Before answering this question, the doctors to whom I addressed it dwelt on the impossibility today, over fifty years after the subject's death, with only literary evidence to go on, of stating anything absolutely definite, as proven or incontrovertible. But they were also at one in saying that the available data on Dino Campana suggested syphilis, 'nervous syphilis', in fact, which he had contracted in Genoa in February 1912 and entered its third phase a little over three years later, in the summer of 1915. I am told that this kind of syphilis is transmitted by a micro-organism called *Spirochaeta pallida* Schandinnii, that it presents roughly the same symptoms as meningitis, and that asylum practice up to the 1930s and 1940s regarded it as an ordinary form of 'dementia' to be treated by electric shock therapy, beatings, strapping the patient to his bed, enforced isolation...

March 1906. Dino Campana follows Regolo first to Pavia and then to Milan: he helps him with his trade (perhaps sewing kits, perhaps neck-ties or other things) and receives his advice on the art of survival, of getting across frontiers, of eluding the police forces of every nation. The two stay together for ten or twelve days, then Dino goes to Porta Tosa station, where the trains leave for Switzerland, and stows away on board a goods-train bound for Bellinzona. He walks over the St Gotthard Pass (the lakes, the 'bright pools' which he sees as he rises 'among the rocks', are precisely the small lakes just below the top of the St Gotthard) and enters German-speaking Switzerland. Sleeping wherever he chances to be, and eating as he walks, he reaches Zurich and Basle. Here he finds himself right out of money, looks for work at the entertainment park, falls in with some gypsies. As he later tells Pariani: 'I sold sparklers at fun-fairs. The Bosyaky are like gypsies. Round about we sold calendars, sparklers. They're roaming companies of five or six people. The shooting gallery was in Switzerland.' It's pretty muddled evidence, but it suggests that in Basle (or Zurich) Dino helps run a shooting booth, and that when the booth-owners move on, he accompanies them, hawking their wares; and over into France. The *Canti Orfici* take up the chronicle: 'I still see Paris, place d'Italie, the stalls, the caravans, the gaunt cavaliers of the unreal, their faces shrivelled, their eyes piercing with fierce nostalgia, the whole huge square blazing with an infernal concert, strident and irritating, the Bohémiens' little girls, their hair hanging loose, the deep pools of their fearless eyes frozen in ambiguous rueful weariness around the smooth deserted pond. And last, Her, unmindful, remote, love, her gypsy face in the billowing sounds and lights tinged with unreal enchantment; and us silent around the pond's ruddy brilliances; and us again weary of the dream wandering aimlessly through unknown districts to stretch ourselves out wearily at last on a bed in a distant tavern amid the warm breath of vice; us there in our uncertainty and our regretfulness tinging our lust with unreal glintings!'

That bed in the 'distant tavern' is Dino's last memory of France: for of far-famed Paris, world capital of art and culture, he sees nothing. Between the fifth and the ninth of May he suddenly reappears in Marradi: having been repatriated by the French gendarmerie for having no passport and handed over to the Italian police at Fréjus or one of the other passes into Piedmont. The 'great escape' is over.

Let us take a backward step to salvage a part of the story which has been lost. Let us go back to the Campana household towards the end of February. Dino has disappeared. Fanny formulates no hypotheses, shows no emotion: she reacts to circumstances by wrapping herself up in her silence, in her shawl, in her usual prayers. Not so Dino's father. Indifferent at first, partly thanks to his brother Torquato's advice ('You'll see he's gone to the whore-house'), on the third day after his son's disappearance he hastens to Bologna, to the University, to look for him: he discovers that he's ploughed his physics exam and imagines the worst, he despairs. He rails at his wife: 'You're the one who tormented him, who made life impossible for him.' At himself: 'It's me. It's my own fault. I'm a monster.' On the fifth day of Dino's absence – this is, of course, an 'imaginative' reconstruction of events – after a night spent smoking his cigars and pacing the house, Giovanni goes back to Bologna to report the disappearance of Campana Dino, a 'minor' aged twenty, born and resident in Marradi and studying chemistry at the University. Rumours are going round Marradi: 'The schoolmaster's son has died.' 'The elder one, the one who's slightly mad.' 'No, no, he's simply made off.' 'He's failed an exam and then disappeared.' 'He was seen last along the Lamone river.' 'Jesus and Mary, so young!' 'He was found on the railway line. He couldn't be identified because his head was gone.' Marianna and Barberina put on mourning, which means eliminating any remaining touch of colour from their clothing, already mostly black. Parents of young scallywags or scatterbrains warn their offspring: 'You'll end up the same way as the schoolmaster's son!'

Days go by, weeks, months. A heavy, almost sombre, atmosphere hangs over the Campana household: Giovanni and Fanny exchange not a word, and even Manlio stays in as little as he can. At the beginning of April, Giovanni returns once more to the central police station in Bologna to enquire whether they have news of his son. He is told there is none, and bursts out sobbing: 'He's dead by now.' 'He's been missing a month and a half, without money or papers. How can he be alive?' A commissioner, feeling sorry for him, gets up, goes and rests a hand on his arm. 'Your son's alive, believe me. If he were dead we'd have found him. It's because he's alive that we haven't found him.'

Dino reappears in Marradi and people stare at him in the street as though they were looking at a ghost. He enters the Croce Bianca café, but the proprietor throws him out: 'I don't want any trouble. Be off, be off!' At home, he seeks refuge in his Uncle Torquato's apartment, where he faces his first interrogation: 'Where have you been? What have you been up to?' 'Who's been supporting you while you've been abroad?' On the floor above, tragedy erupts: screams, the crash of crockery. The 'spirited' Fanny Campana wants to pack her bags and leave for good. Giovanni restrains her and promises to take his son to the lunatic asylum the very next day. He says: 'This time I'll have him put away in the asylum and I'll leave him there as long as he lives because when someone behaves as he's done he's either a delinquent or a lunatic. To keep us in such anxiety for over two months without sending us a word, a line!' An expert at making arrangements, he plans it all out. He tells his wife: 'Tomorrow being Thursday, I'm free from school. I'll go with Dino to Bologna: first I'll take him to the police station, as the commissioner might want to question him; then I'll have a report done on him by one of the medical luminaries, whoever, by Murri or his assistant Vitali: someone to whom they can't refuse a committal. So on my way back via Imola I'll leave him in Brugia's care.'

On the following day, 10 May, Giovanni carries out his plan and reappears in Marradi that evening with his son: whose committal, he explains to a glowering Fanny, has

encountered unforeseen obstacles and will have to be post-
poned. 'First and foremost,' says the schoolmaster, 'Professor Vitali, who examined him, asked me rather a lot of
questions of a certain kind... Whether we're forcing him
to study against his will; whether we badger him at home;
whether he's on good terms with his mother. Just listen to
what he's written to Brugia.' He extracts Vitali's letter from
his pocket, puts on his glasses. He reads out: 'The psychic
condition is one of over-excitation... bromides are to be
administered...' Ah, here we are: 'Insist that his family
leave him in peace.' He lays the letter down on the table.
'It almost sounds as though it were our fault that he's over-
excited...' Fanny makes an impatient gesture: 'So?'
Giovanni stretches his arms apart. 'So there's nothing
doing. We went to the asylum in Imola and there they told
me that before admitting him they have to wait till he's
twenty-one, they don't admit minors.' He remains silent
for a moment, then relates: 'Brugia wasn't there. I spoke
to one of his assistants, who explained to me the way things
are now that there's this new law on asylums. He said I
could have saved myself the consultation with Vitali, his
letter is of no consequence. In little more than three months'
time, Brugia's assistant told me, your son will reach his
majority and all that's needed to commit him is for the
Marradi medical officer to fill in a form which every public
health office is legally bound to have. Just as was done in
my brother's case, remember? The mayor issues the order,
then the carabinieri call at the patient's house to take charge
of him; they are the ones, nowadays, who take patients
away to the asylum.'

The examination by Professor Vitali on 10 May 1906; the letter to Brugia which schoolmaster Campana secures in the belief that it is a prerequisite for his son's confinement, and which is not passed on to the addressee until 13 September, by which time Dino is already in the asylum; the very close correspondence between Dino's birthday and the date of his committal; and finally the choice, in preference to the Florence asylum, which would be normal, of the Imola psychiatric institution, 'at the family's option', as allowed by article 46 of the law of 14 February 1904, No 6: everything suggests that in having their twenty-one-year-old son locked up in a madhouse Fanny and Giovanni Campana were putting into effect a plan which had been elaborated months earlier and perfected with the help of the town worthies, namely, the Mayor, land-surveyor Giovanni Balocco, the medical officer, Dr Augusto Pellegrini, the pharmacist, the station-master, the director of the post office... Early twentieth-century Marradi, like any other Italian provincial town, has its own club of local worthies (the 'Circolo Marradese', with premises on Piazza Scalelle), which roughly corresponds to the active or passive electorate of the area or, to use the poet Gozzano's words, 'politics' illustrious / local academy'. To this society of literate male well-to-do townsfolk, Dino has belonged by right since the day he was born; and it is this same 'Circolo Marradese' that acts as his custodian and guardian through the summer of 1906 while he awaits his coming of age in order to be admitted to the Imola madhouse. It is the 'townspeople' of Marradi who undertake the provisional care of the 'madman'. The town hall has a photograph showing Dino with the local dignitaries in the hills. It carries no date nor any other information and – judging by the appearance of the poet and that of schoolmaster Campana – may have been taken during the summer of 1906 or of the following year at the latest...

Dino, by the laws of the time, comes of age on 20 August 1906, his twenty-first birthday. On Monday, 3 September, like Pinocchio between the gendarmes, he goes to the station to catch the train to Imola. There is an 'information sheet' to be filled in by the medical officer on these occasions. There are only four known entries regarding Dino, which I transcribe complete. The left-hand column shows the printed questionnaire and the right-hand column the doctor's hand-written answers:

Physical and moral causes of madness.	Addicted to coffee for which he is extremely greedy and which he consumes to extraordinary excess.
Current symptomatic manifestations, both physical and psychic, of madness.	Psychic excitation. Impulsiveness and vagrancy.
Diagnosis of the form of madness and, if possible, of nature of same.	Precocious dementia?
Statement of reasons why undersigned doctor deems it necessary for the lunatic to be confined and cared for in an Asylum.	So as to remove him from the dangers of his impulsively irritable condition and because of his vagrancy which might expose him to serious danger.

Apart from this last answer, which is self-explanatory, some remarks and marginal notes are called for. For instance, regarding coffee as the only *physical and moral cause of madness*, it must be pointed out that there is no other evidence, from either an earlier or a later date, of 'a quite exceptional degree' of abuse of coffee on Dino's part; in fact it appears that he subsequently changed to drinking tea. (Letter to Anstrid Anhfelt: 'Might I ask you to include a packet or two of Hornigham's tea.' Letter to Sibilla Aleramo: 'Send me a quarter kilo of the The Hornimas sole joy.') It is also interesting to observe that from this report of 1906 Dino appears to be a teetotaller, whilst in that of 1909 – where there is no mention of coffee – the word 'alcoholism' is used. As regards the *symptomatic manifestations*, the Marradi medical officer relies in part on Vitali's authority ('The psychic condition is one of over-excitation'), and in part reports his father's concern as confided to him: the word 'impulsiveness' in particular refers to family rows and is the word used by the schoolmaster himself. Finally, regarding the *diagnosis*, the term 'dementia praecox' has disappeared from psychiatric use and never designated any scientifically tenable phenomenon, but merely a form of 'dementia', so called – say the handbooks of the period – 'because of its appearance earlier than other forms'. (In practice, *dementia praecox* could be attributed to a child-prostitute as well as to a brain-damaged child or a maladjusted adolescent who had committed a crime).

Let us enter the Imola mental asylum with Dino. Let us watch his belongings being itemized, his skull being shaved, his disinfecting all over, his robing in a ridiculous uniform, loose and short, made of brown wool. 'It fits you like a glove,' the orderly assures him. His being weighed and measured by Brugia's assistant. (Who is quite likely to remark: 'Trochocephalic. Denotes homicidal tendencies.') Picture the interior, with its corridors, its large rooms, the bars on all the windows, the chains on all the beds, the cess-buckets, the stench, the caterwauling. Imagine the inmates, whom asylum language indiscriminately designates 'lunatics' and who should really be divided into at least two categories, the downfallen and the degenerate. The downfallen ('downfallen folk', as Dino Campana calls them) are those who, being relatively normal to start with, still retain even in the madhouse a glimmering of sense and a modicum of dignity. You can tell them apart from the degenerate because they do not try to copulate, they go to the latrines to relieve themselves, refuse to eat their food if it contains cockroaches or worms, attend to their personal cleanliness and in some cases are capable of sustaining a conversation, asking or answering questions aptly. Before entering the asylum they may have been epileptics, alcoholics, eccentrics, manic-depressives who have proved too much for their families, revolutionaries without a revolution, inventors without inventions; now the environment has assimilated them and stamped out the last traces of their individuality. The degenerate, on the other hand, are those 'lunatics' who have compounded their original affliction with so-called 'asylum lunacy' and have lost all the better characteristics of man and beast. Their behaviour is aberrant no matter what form it takes, from the absolute lethargy of the idiots to the convulsive aggressiveness of those who are 'a danger to themselves and to others'. The asylum is a hell on earth for this very reason, namely, that it forces upon each other the downfallen and the degenerates and 'lunatics' of every category. This forced association – according to the law of 1904 which I have quoted several times already – is not supposed to include the temporary inmates, who are, in fact, to be kept scrupulously segregated from the rest, and even prevented from seeing them. ('During the period when asylum inmates are under observation,' reads article 58 of the Regulations, 'they must be kept constantly in their own quarters. . . Breach of this regulation, unless justified by absolute necessity, will be penalized by a fine to be paid by the Director, of between Lire 20 and Lire 100.') But in small institutions like the one in Imola the segregation between 'temporary' and 'permanent' inmates is more a fiction than a reality: it applies to dormitories, but not to latrines or day-rooms or the two or three corridors where the lunatics of every sort are bound to spend their waking hours, inevitably mixing together . . .

Being normal, Dino reacts to asylum life by alternating between despondency and fury: he rebels and gets beatings, he rages and is strapped to his bed; in a word, he behaves 'like a madman'. Brugia applies for a court order to declare him a permanent inmate (this file is, unfortunately, lost). The Bologna court, on the basis of Brugia's diagnosis, declares Dino a lunatic. It instructs the patient's parents to appoint a guardian, and, at this point, if there were no new development, the story of Dino Campana would end like a fairy-tale, with him living unhappily ever after, rescued once and for all from his 'impulsive irritability' and 'vagrancy'. But a new development is brought about by his relatives who go to see him in Imola and return distraught. 'How's Dino? Better?' asks his father somewhat crassly. They cringe. 'Yes...' they say, 'perhaps so.' 'He's in such a state, poor boy...' Troubled, Giovanni Campana makes the momentous decision. He goes to Imola: he sees the establishment, the orderlies, the 'patients', his emaciated, battered son who throws himself at his feet, kneeling, sobbing, begging him to get him out of this place, for charity's sake: to save him. Who kisses his hands and says: 'I will never bother anyone again, I'll go to America, to Australia, to places where people emigrate for good. I swear.' White-faced, the schoolmaster seems on the point of fainting: and truly it has to be said that, like all those who favour the most ruthless of final solutions, he is, when it comes to the point, so chicken-livered that he can't stand the sight of blood and won't enter a hospital because – he says – the medical odours make him dizzy...He blows his nose, loosens his tie. Flees. Returns to Marradi and reports back to his wife on what he's seen: the place, the inmates, Dino's condition, his desperation. 'It's for his own good,' she returns coolly. 'That's the only place where he'll get better.' But when she realizes that her husband is seriously intending to apply for his son's release, she starts packing her bags. She tries her usual threats: 'If he comes back here, I leave.'

Towards mid-October the schoolmaster writes to the asylum director requesting him to authorize his deranged son's 'release on a trial basis' as allowed by law: I myself, he says, will ensure that he is supervised and cared for under instructions from you. Brugia appears reluctant. 'After two months' constant observation I must confirm that your son is seriously psychopathic and that his prospects of recovery are extremely problematical. He would be in no state to be released from the Asylum, as he is still far from recovery; but, bearing in mind your insistence in asking for his return home, the special arrangements you are making for his seclusion in the country, and also the patient's own eager and indeed almost excessive desire to leave this place, I will not oppose your withdrawing him from the Asylum on a trial basis. But to that end it is necessary for you to come here in person and make out on the spot a signed statement undertaking full responsibility for any possible eventuality arising from your son's restoration to liberty.'

On 31 October 1906 (a Thursday, as usual) Dino returns to Marradi, badly shaken by his experience of the Imola asylum: and now he is an officially certified lunatic, no longer his own master but obliged to act in every matter through his guardian. The relevant documents are unfortunately missing, but his guardian is appointed towards the end of the year, and the person appointed is the lunatic's uncle, Torquato Campana. Why? Why does schoolmaster Giovanni, after his meeting with Brugia, decline to act as his son's legal guardian? Why does he, from 31 October 1906 onwards, display a fear of the very same psychiatrist who had previously 'cured' him? In order to answer these questions we would need to know what Brugia told him about his son's condition and the likelihood that there is a hereditary connection with Giovanni's 'neurasthenic disorders'. About the nature and characteristics of these latter, which the schoolmaster had believed cured but which, Brugia warns, are liable to recur, even decades later. 'Heredity admits of no cure. At most it allows periods of dormancy.' The law of 1904 allows asylum directors to conduct inquiries into the mental health of members of a patient's family: and it is my hunch that Brugia took the opportunity to advise the schoolmaster to undergo regular psychiatric examinations or even a brief pre-emptive stay in the Imola asylum. 'You need only sign an application and I will keep you under strict observation for a month.'

On 11 November 1906 Dino is officially declared unfit,

as a lunatic, for military service. The Conscription Register shows rubber-stamped dates recording Dino as *Suspended* and then *Released* (11 November 1906); *Confirmed* (10 February 1907). The file is sealed and signed by one Alfredo Saccini and is not opened even when the class of '85 is called up for the war. But these developments take place without the knowledge of the party concerned, who, as soon as he is back in Marradi, shuts himself away in his room. He says nothing, ignores his brother's overtures, does not show himself around the town. He sits for hours on end staring at nothing. He feels like a nothing himself, as if something important in himself had been lost. As if all certainty had finally deserted him. 'I'm a ruin, *une épave*.' The cause of all his misfortunes he sees in his own mysterious 'difference': 'There's no room for me in this perfected machinery which is society: I'm the faulty part which the fitter discards. The pollen grain that does not set fruit but carpets the forest floor.' Without delusions or misgivings he ponders a second escape, one that is final and legal, arranged with his parents. Towards a landfall so beyond reach of recall as to prefigure that ultimate landfall, death: 'As I walk down the street, so I will go across the world; I have no ties, no loads to bear; hanging on to life like the autumn leaf on the tree.'

Fanny Campana regains her calm. Dino, her husband tells her, will be off to Australia or America, somewhere far away where even someone different like him can find his feet. 'You must believe me, Fanny. The asylum is no place to have a son. It's like being buried alive.' – A tireless deviser of final solutions which destiny punctiliously makes it its business to nullify, the schoolmaster Giovanni Campana once again sets to work 'settling' his son. He sends a letter to Buenos Aires, to a Marradi family who have gone out there: he lists Dino's misadventures and says that his son now wants to make a fresh start in the New World, far from the complications and snags that have made him unsuccessful over here. Would you help him find a job? The letter travels towards its distant destination. Life in Marradi proceeds in its usual monotonous way, the same cycle of seasons, unvarying and – say the old farmers – 'no longer the same as the seasons used to be'. Autumn, and then winter: snow, children tobogganing, the torrent frozen in its bed, the feasting at the turn of the year, the bitter, polar cold of the 'blackbird days' at the end of January and of early February. Winter ends with the thaw. But as the thaw starts a letter is delivered to the Campanas' house that bears a strange stamp with the legend: *Argentina. Republica de Argentina.* A note inside the envelope written in 'indelible' pencil says fine, send us your son, if he's sturdy and means business he'll fit in same as everybody. We undertake to give him a bed and find him an honest livelihood. Give our greetings to Marradi. *Addio.* The signature, the writer's name and surname, unfortunately cannot be identified: no one remembers them and the *Comune* of Marradi doesn't hold lists of emigrants. But there *was* a letter, and that Dino did go to Argentina by epistolary agreement and with his passage paid is doubly certain: first, because the testimony of all his relations (his brother Manlio, his cousin Nello, his aunt Giovanna Diletti) is unanimous on this point; secondly, because the authorities in Florence would not have issued a passport under the name of Dino Campana unless guarantees had been given that the 'lunatic' was going to join friends, perhaps even relatives. It is safe to say that Dino travelled to Buenos Aires like a parcel: handed over by his guardian to the ship's captain (family memories specify that Torquato accompanied his nephew 'right on board ship'); then by the ship's captain to the anonymous Marradi man who was waiting for him on the quay, lost among that throng of emigrants whom Dino, as he arrived, saw 'ridiculously dressed, Buenos Aires fashion'.

The schoolmaster's greatest difficulty in posting the parcel is obtaining the passport, even though his brother the magistrate's visiting card opens all the doors in the Florence Questura. The reply is always the same: sorry, we can't authorize a 'lunatic' to leave the country. What you have to do – the officials tell Campana – is apply to the director of the asylum where your son was admitted and ask him to send the papers for his release to the court... For weeks and months the business of the passport goes round in circles which always lead back to that Brugia who considers hereditary complaints incurable and who, early in May, is still asking the mayor of Marradi, 'under the Law of 14 February 1904, No 36, and of art. 66, paragraph 4, of the Regulation concerned', to send him every four months a certificate from the medical officer 'attesting to the condition of the lunatic Campana Dino son of Giovanni and Luti Francesca, who has been permanently admitted into this Asylum'. (Further to this request, a statement by Dr Pellegrini is sent from Marradi on 25 May 1907, saying that he had 'examined Campana Dino and found his mental condition much improved. He no longer suffers deliriums, and his family also report that his psychic functions have become very normal.')

The passport to Argentina is finally issued with an additional note explaining that the holder is 'insane' and unable to travel without his guardian. The photograph taken for the purpose is the well-known one in which Dino has his hair parted on the right and a pencil-thin handle-bar moustache. His lips hint at the smile the photographer asked for, but the expression in his eyes remains uncertain, half cross and half sad. The date – September 1907 – figures in the records of the Florence Questura, or police headquarters, and is therefore reliable.

Dino Campana goes to America, probably in October 1907, at his parents' bidding and has his passage paid for him. ('*Zavoli:* Let me put you a proposition which you might think absurd: what if Dino Campana never went to Argentina? *Manlio Campana:* The poor fellow's head was full of delusions and fantasies, but that journey wasn't just his doing . . .') He goes under duress and out of fear of landing in the madhouse again. He goes with his heart bursting with homesickness for his Marradi where 'the priests bellow their chants like oxen' but where, also, 'there is beautiful vegetation. The deep blue of the sky meets the Tuscan light, morning and evening, along the mountain fringes. The river is beautiful.' A few days before his departure he disappears without trace. '*Manlio Campana:* When Dino's passage to America was arranged, Dino came to Florence. Papa didn't feel up to seeing him as far as his ship in Genoa, and entrusted him to the care of a brother, our uncle. I remember that he had to wait two days because I just couldn't find him! I knew Dino was in Florence, but I couldn't find him because he kept eluding me. At last I managed to meet him, to persuade him, to tell him that his uncle was here, waiting for him. So he took the plunge and went off with his uncle who took him right on board the ship that was to transport him to Argentina.

'The legend that he led a roving life and saved up to pay his passage, by all sorts of odd jobs, is a tall story that needs to be dismissed, put right.

'Dino travelled out with a job already waiting for him. In Buenos Aires he moved in with a family to live, planted his luggage there, stayed a day and a night, but from the dawn of the second day, never went back. He sent someone to collect his luggage and left for the Pampas. What *is* true, because he confirmed the fact to me himself, is that he worked his passage back on a merchant ship. As a stoker, from what I could gather! Handling coal, mostly. He landed in Amsterdam.'

In Genoa, before boarding ship, Dino still keeps jibbing. He wants books, then a revolver. Torquato refuses to buy him one; so he says 'I'll see you in the harbour' and vanishes into the crowd. Giovanna Diletti Campana, Torquato's wife: 'They arranged to meet in the harbour. But hours went by, and Dino was not to be seen. Imagine poor Torquato's anxiety and distress, the ship was just about to sail. At last Dino arrived just in time to go on board. In America he did all sorts of jobs, deckhand and what-have-you. When he returned from America he was dressed in seaman's clothes, with a broad blue sash around his waist. He looked handsome and was in very good spirits.'

What ship takes Dino to America we do not know: but does it matter? Certainly it's a vessel very similar to the *Galileo* as described by De Amicis in his story 'Sull'oceano', if not the very same. It could be any of the 'misery hulks' that ply between Genoa and Montevideo, and if Dino does not name it, that is because it belongs to a mode of writing that does not interest him and which he experiences 'without joy'. 'There were two poor girls on the stern deck: Lady Distress, we belong to Lady Distress: you won't see Genoa lighthouse again, you won't! What did it matter anyway! I thought. Let the boat dance, let the boat dance all the way to Buenos-Aires, it livened things up and the sea laughed with us, its oh so sly and comic laugh. And the misery hulk danced and danced upon the infinite. But I don't know if it was sea-sickness or disgust which caused my own laughter: certainly it was the irritating numskullery, that great numskull laughing so numskullishly that roused my laughter: then my laughter or my stomach had calmed down: days went by: sky and water, sky and water: I stared at the day from my refuge among the potato sacks. Later, stretched out wearily on the deck I could see the masthead swaying at the stars in the warm night amidst the noise of water: and at times through the porthole which the waves often reached I had followed the equatorial sunset on the sea. Birds were winging far from their nests and I too but without joy. We were hugging the coast: I remember, the sunset lit up the deserted *campo* with its last red rays and the sun set beyond the deserted coast.'

So, that's all there is to Dino's voyage to America: twenty-four days at sea, Genoa, the Cape Verde islands ('A white town slumbering / At the feet of the towering peaks of the extinct volcanoes'), Montevideo, 'sea-capital' of the new continent, Buenos Aires, 'grey and veiled' with its 'strange' harbour where the emigrés grow 'crazed' and 'wild' cramming the quay where the steamer will moor. The only noteworthy things about that world are the immense unpeopled spaces, the 'impassive stars, above the infinitely deserted and mysterious earth'. The only problem is that of getting away, returning 'towards the calm oases of old Europe's sensibility'. In Buenos Aires, a town which he finds absolutely foreign to him, Dino stays just a few days, just long enough to discover that the boats for Europe sail from Bahia Blanca and that that is where he has to go if he wants to be taken on. He has no immediate money problems. He works a little, here and there, mostly to while away the time and to get to know people. 'I played the triangle in the Argentine navy,' he will tell Pariani years later. 'I was a doorkeeper for a Buenos Aires circus.' 'I was a policeman in Argentina, that is, a fireman.' Are we to believe him? Yes. With this reservation: that he gave his services occasionally, and for very brief periods. From one day to a week; sometimes, just for a few hours. 'At the Ministry for the Mercantile Marine,' writes Cacho Millet, 'I was informed that *there is no record of Mr Dino Campana belonging to the band*. "At that time," the ex-chief of the Buenos Aires harbour police, Luis Bongiovanni, explained to me as if by way of consolation, "immigrants 'contracted' just to play an instrument, and then left the band simply by not turning up again."'

December 1907. An official document is sent from the Marradi town hall to the Imola asylum attesting to the departure for America, with his guardian's consent, of Signor Dino Campana: 'About whom this health authority can therefore furnish no further information.' In South America, December is the first month of summer and Dino cannot resist the temptation to have a look round, before returning to Europe; to see the *pampas* and the Andes. He signs on as a road worker, a *peón de via*, for a British firm building railways, using local labour – creoles and immigrants especially. 'I've piled up the railway embankments in Argentina,' the poet will tell Pariani. 'You camp out. The work's easy but monotonous.' Among the places he visited he names 'Santa Rosa de Toay in the middle of Argentina' and Mendoza near the Andes, in fact he says of Mendoza: 'Round Mendoza they produce wine as in Italy.'

What is a *peón*'s work? 'First an embankment was made, using earth from nearby without any gravel, and the sleepers were laid. Finally the rails were fixed on to the sleepers with special bolts. Besides that, the poles for taking the telegraph wires were erected... Everything was imported from England. Only the earth was Argentinian. The manpower consisted mostly of immigrants. We shifted camp periodically as the line advanced. Everything was carried to the spot on goods trains – rails as well as sleepers, bolts and other metal parts. Often, the workmen travelled on the same train...' This is not Campana's story; it's the testimony of one of the *peones*, which Cacho Millet discovered and published. For Dino, the experience of those days is condensed into a few images of extraordinary intensity which are fixed in the prose-piece *Pampa*: the *peones* seated in a ring amidst their tents drinking *mate*, the train's night run, the 'infinite sky undefiled by Any God's shadow'. But it goes without saying, also, that in the everyday 'monotony', other things go on. There are dealings with workmates, there's the language to be learnt, or rather, languages: Spanish, English... (During the Great War, when he decides to give up 'literature in every form' and find himself a job, Dino thinks of earning his living by putting to use just this knowledge of foreign languages. So he writes on his letters: 'Dino Campana. Translator from English, German, Spanish, French. Sanesi Hotel – Lastra a Signa – Florence.')

In late February or early March of 1908, when Campana arrives in Bahia Blanca, he finds it's a port on the pampas as well as a port on the ocean, which is a few kilometres away. 'The prairie rose like a silvery sea in the background, and jetsam from that sea, down-and-outs, fierce men, men unknown shut within their dark will, bloody tales at once to be forgotten which suddenly came back to life in the night, wove around me the story of the fierce young town, implacable all-conquering burning with a high fever for money and instant joys.' Dino spends less than a month in this Far West setting, living off the money which he has earned on the pampas and going down to the harbour from time to time to find out about the ships leaving for Europe. He comes across Regolo Orlandelli, the tramp whom he had met in the Po Valley fog with his 'coat-collar pulled up around his ears'. Regolo has an 'employment agency' – that is, a wooden shack where every morning at dawn the hopeless, the luckless, those who have gambled away their last farthing during the night come to queue up...Unlike Dino, he is earnest: he's come seeking his fortune and – so he says – intends to find it. He is one of the numerous 'fierce men' who people Bahia Blanca, 'shut within their dark will'. He talks of capital, investments, fortunes piled up within a few weeks. He cannot understand what drives Dino to seek a passage back to Europe: 'But haven't they bust your balls back home, haven't they locked you away in the madhouse!' Dino smiles. The idea of staying on in America to make money is not something he can consider seriously, but he enjoys listening to Regolo's plans. And Regolo digs his heels in. To keep him from leaving, to show him that even on this side of the ocean you don't have to live like a *peón*, he secures engagements for him as a pianist. 'I played the piano in Argentina,' Dino relates twenty years later, 'whenever I was out of money; I played in taverns, in brothels. Then I used to go wandering round the country-side.'

His chance to return to Europe comes towards mid-April: a stoker's job on the merchantman *Odessa*, bound for Antwerp. (Pariani's report of a voyage to Odessa is cock-and-bull, and has no place in Campana biography; nor is it conceivable, as Dino's brother Manlio suggested, that Odessa was a port of call on the way from Bahia Blanca to Antwerp. For three very good reasons. First, Odessa lies in quite another direction from Antwerp; because Dino mentioned to the writer Soffici another and much likelier port of call, Dover, in England; and finally because reaching Odessa means crossing the Aegean and seeing Istanbul and the Orient: places of which there is no trace in Campana's writings... The impossible voyage, akin to the 'mad exploit' of Dante's Ulysses, known only to Pariani, is the fruit of a howler on the part of the biographer: misinterpreting the ship's name, he takes Dino to say 'I went to Odessa' instead of 'I went on the *Odessa*'. Let me say, to restore the truth, that a merchant steamer, the *Odessa*, dismantled after the First World War, was in fact registered in the British Merchant Navy during the early years of the century; and that it was precisely on that steamship that Dino, by all the evidence, returned from America in the spring of 1908, 'handling coal'...)

During his month as a stoker on the *Odessa* Dino shovels coal, practises deciphering the sounds of the English language and, during his rest periods as he lies on his bunk, he goes over the plans he made in faraway Bahia Blanca, he perfects his dream in detail. He'll go to Paris, the city he barely glimpsed and never really knew, from which he was deported two years back. He'll get some work or other and stay put as long as it takes to produce that book of 'poems and prose tales' which is to be the 'meaning' and the 'justification' of his life. Then he'll go back to Italy to print it. – In mid-May he lands at Antwerp; he walks as far as Brussels, where something happens which lands him in gaol. 'On my way back to Italy,' Dino later tells the tireless Pariani, 'as I was passing through Belgium, I was arrested and held in a cell; for two months, at Saint-Gilles. Some people there were mad and some weren't. Then I was shut away in Tournai in some kind of nursing-home, because I wasn't fixed up anywhere, I was restless, a rolling stone. It was a refuge for down-and-outs, a sort of madhouse.'

Like the one month's imprisonment in Parma, these two months in a cell in Brussels, in the fortress-prison of Saint-Gilles, come down to just one night of preventive detention: it leaves no trace in prison registers or in the Italian consular archive. And perhaps one should explain what preventive detention means in Europe at the start of the century. Certain people (vagrants, con-men, bums, sailors and suchlike) are rounded up off the streets after dark and locked up for the night in prison: not because they have committed any crime, but lest an excess of liberty lead them into temptation. In some countries, including Italy, the arrangement is so benign that the tramps themselves resort to it so as to save the expense of lodgings: every prison sees someone or other turn himself in by a reasonable time of night and then leave in the morning, painfully stiff from the bedboards but with finances (and reputation) intact. Dino Campana, wandering around Brussels in his striking seaman's clothes, 'with a broad blue sash around his waist', must have run into trouble more or less of this kind. He runs into more serious trouble at the French border, where he is turned back because his passport is not valid for entry into France and because its holder is defined as a 'lunatic' who may not travel unless accompanied by his guardian. Where is the guardian? There is no guardian. The French gendarmes hand Dino back to the Belgians and the latter – since he is a madman – lock him up in the nearest asylum, that is, the *Maison de santé 'Saint-Bernard'* in Tournai, a few kilometres from the border. Obliged by circumstances to turn once again to his father, Dino writes home (and the family in fact recollects the schoolmaster Giovanni receiving a letter from his son 'while he was in Argentina'): he asks to have his identity confirmed and his journey back home paid for. At first his father just will not hear of it. He will not forgive him for having tried to cut himself off from his family; for having wanted to dispose of his own life of his own accord. He says (as family memoirs have it): 'It wasn't me who sent him where he is now. He wanted to go there, so let him stay there.' In the end he relents and authorizes his son's return home: Torquato Campana, the 'lunatic''s guardian makes the request to the Belgian authorities. Early in July Dino is back in Marradi: and, according to his aunt Giovanna Diletti, he looks 'handsome' and 'in very good spirits', that is, glad to see the light of Tuscany again, the mountains, the landscape. 'See the rocks, strata upon strata, memorials to solitary tenacity that console the hearts of men. And sweet seemed my fugitive destiny under the spell of the distant mirages of adventure which still beckon smilingly from the azure mountains: and upon hearing the water murmuring beneath the naked rocks, still cool from the depths of earth. So I know a music sweet in my memory without recalling a single note: I know it's called departure or homecoming: I know a picture lost in the splendour of Florentine art with its word of sweet nostalgia: it's the prodigal son shaded by the trees of his father's house. Literature? I cannot tell. My memory, the water, is just like that.' Certainly, there is still conflict with his mother, people in Marradi treat him as mad: but on seeing once again the 'mystical valley' of the Lamone, on seeing Campigno again, Dino realizes all at once that only in these high places does his heart 'quiver with vertigo'. ('*Don Pietro Poggiolini*: More than the people, it was the country where he was born that he loved. I shouldn't like to say anything that might perhaps tarnish the honour of Marradi, but I believe it's just as I've said! *Zavoli*: Marradi did so little for Campana! *Don Pietro Poggiolini*: Nothing, nothing, nothing, nothing, nothing, nothing, nothing!')

Dino probably spends two or three weeks in Tournai, a month at most. No record remains: documents and buildings and all were destroyed twice over in the two World Wars and the asylum itself has changed its name and is now called *Hôpital psychiatrique de l'Etat 'Les Marronniers'*. From Dino's writings and recollections we can say that at Tournai he finds the same 'ordeal of mud' he came to know in Imola, but in a more bearable, almost acceptable form. The 'down-and-outs' here are kept apart from the 'real lunatics' and the indolent and sadistic orderlies are replaced by 'grey friars of serene – too serene – countenance'. (The asylum is at this time run by the Frères de la Charité Chrétienne.) Among the 'down-and-outs' is 'the Russian violinist and painter', prophet of an obscure social creed which somehow or other is supposed to be summed up in the following parable: 'A man, alone in his house on a December night, feels the terror of his solitude. He thinks perhaps there are people outside dying of cold: and he goes out to rescue them. In the morning, when he gets back, alone, he finds a woman at his door, frozen to death. And he kills himself.' This character, tall and gaunt, with his long, reddish beard, makes a deep impression on Dino's fantasy, The *Canti Orfici* imagine him murdered by the friars. ('As Belgium has no legal extradition for political offenders, the office was carried out by the Brothers of Christian Charity.') Many years later, under interrogation by Pariani, Dino remembers a detail which is absent from that prose passage of the *Canti*

Orfici: in order to conceal his identity, the Russian pretended to have lost his memory, to have forgotten his name. Dino speaks of him circumspectly: 'Well...he'd attacked...well ...I'm not quite sure what he did...He was one of those numerous Russians who roam the world, who don't know what to do. They're intellectuals up to a point, they write, they do one thing or another, they mostly starve to death. They find new ideas abroad, they plot together to modernize Russia, and get sent to Siberia.'

Dino's 'good spirits' during the summer of 1908 are attested by Torquato's daughter Maria ('Mimma'): born in 1899, she is now just nine years old. Ravagli: 'He enjoyed playing with her and occasionally would put his hands round her neck as if to lift her up bodily, which he in fact did, to the great concern of the girl's mother, who was afraid he might hurt her. Dino was then strongly built, with slightly wavy blond hair and of merry humour: he always had a smile for the little girl and was kind to her; he was always good-natured with everyone at home.' One day while Dino is in the garden 'Mimma' gives him some paper and says: 'Write something for me.' And Dino, after a moment's hesitation, writes a French poem with the beginning of the Italian translation alongside it. ('I a poor Paris troubadour / Offer you only a bouquet of flimsy verses / Be kind to me and on the simple live lips / I know, descend, trembling kiss, and laugh.') Forty years go by before 'Mimma' learns from the critics that the original poem is Verlaine's 'Le baiser'...

He roams the mountains, secludes himself in certain spots known only to himself, reads, writes. He has no other thought; he ignores all practical issues. Look for work, go away? What would be the use? The inglorious end of his French adventure, and then of his American adventure, has given him precise knowledge of the bond that ties him to his parents and to Marradi. Wherever he goes, sooner or later something will happen to propel him via an asylum back to his family. Serenely, without drama, Dino weighs things up and concludes that the best solution, as far as he is concerned, is to renounce all initiative, to give up thinking about the future; after all, people are already organizing it...'Am I insane or aren't I?' 'Haven't I a father and a guardian who are bound by law to provide for my upkeep?' In his devil-may-care twenties, he adapts to a situation which, for the time being, allows him to do as he pleases without commitments or responsibilities...Yes, he admits he is mad. Not in the clinical sense: but — how to put it? — in the moral sense. In being different from everybody else in a country town – Marradi – where boundary quarrels over a narrow strip of field are carried on from one generation to the next and where the only urge for knowledge concerns other people's business...In being 'a bit primitive', as he readily explains to his friends: 'I act the bear, the freak, only for the benefit of those who lack the elements of sensibility which would make for understanding: from the need to escape from very tiresome...teasing.' 'I'm simply a bit primitive. But we'll be back in fashion, too, that is my hope.'

'I was always off to the countryside to read,' says the poet to Pariani to prove to him that he's mad and should be left where he is. 'I was always up in the mountains writing extravaganzas.' Through the summer and the autumn of 1908, among the pine-trees and the broom-plants and the rocks of Campigno, of the Passo dell'Eremo, of San Benedetto in Alpe, Dino starts ordering the first nucleus of prose-pieces and poetic fragments around which the *Canti Orfici* are to grow: he reworks some texts which he'd written before he went to America, he records impressions and images from his travels. 'I was trying to harmonize some colours, some forms. In the Tuscan landscape I located some memories.' Relations with his parents are reduced to a minimum and in Marradi, too, Dino rarely shows himself. Trouble at home and in the town builds up again when the wintry weather puts an end to mountain walks and open-air poetry: Fanny again starts harping and railing against her firstborn for being 'the bane of her life', 'the family's ruin', 'a disgrace to the household'. Her rows with her husband, at fault for having removed him from the madhouse where he belonged, flare up once more... Dino, who for his part avoids as much as possible talking to his mother and behaves as though she did not exist, sometimes manages to restrain himself but sometimes has much more violently angry outbursts than in the past, smashing furniture and uttering vile imprecations. He accuses both his parents of having wanted him 'mad, willy-nilly', ever since he was a child: with having wanted to stop him from existing, each in their own way and through their own quirks. 'If I'm a nuisance,' he yells at them, 'you only need to free me from your suffocating guardianship and I'll rid you of the bother even tomorrow. Right now.' (His father: 'Dino, be reasonable! You must realize that you, on your own, can't go anywhere. That you're ill.' His mother: 'The madhouse, that's where he must go! To the madhouse, and for good!')

For months and months, through the winter, Dino's only alternative to family delights is the reading room of the 'Circolo Marradese', which however opens only in the afternoons, and the cafés on Piazza Scalelle where people talk about him (the 'madman'), tapping their temples with their forefinger. Where there's always somebody ready to offer him a drink so that he'll get drunk and make a spectacle of himself. . . For the new year of 1909 Dino Campana, now officially designated 'the madman' in local language usage, brings two new phenomena to the life of Marradi: 'the madman' rebels, and 'the madman' drinks. Without showing any enjoyment in drinking, without even noticing the difference between one alcoholic drink and another. With one sole aim: to get drunk. And then, when he's really slewed, it's up to Uncle Torquato (his father, poor chap, 'can't face it') to run out on to the square to rescue him or he'll come to blows with someone or hold forth to the Marradians, accuse his fellow-citizens of being all 'savages', mindless 'brutes'. . . He defies them to emerge from their houses or from the Croce Bianca café to face him. 'Come outside,' he yells at them. 'Come out and say to my face the filth you're putting round about me!'

At the beginning of April of 1909 Fanny runs away from home and schoolmaster Giovanni Campana has a word with Mayor Balocco, Mayor Balocco has a word with Doctor Pellegrini; the chemist, the notary, the director of the post office and the station-master are all of the same opinion: 'the madman' must be put away and kept in an asylum until he has fully recovered. For his own good, first and foremost; and then, as a secondary consideration, for the peace and dignity of his family and the public order of Marradi. Upon his father's suggestion, the local political worthies decide that 'the lad' shall not return to the little asylum in Imola, where he has been unhappy and where he is now believed to be in America. He will go to San Salvi in Florence. 'A first-class asylum,' says Doctor Pellegrini. 'An asylum in which the best psychiatrists in Tuscany are working, perhaps the best in Italy.' The Mayor and the pharmacist also approve the choice: 'If the student Campana has any chance of a cure, surely that's the place.' On Friday 9 April, at eight o'clock in the morning, Dino is sleeping off his hangover from the night before and the *carabinieri* are shaking him, rousing him, making him put on his clothes and follow them – befuddled as he is – to Doctor Pellegrini's surgery, where the doctor has already completed a 'form' in terms that leave no doubt as to the insanity of the subject. (The psychiatrists at San Salvi are left only with the task of 'practical treatment' and precise nomenclature: let them, the experts, say whether this is a case of 'circular madness',

'apoplectic insanity' or, as everything would seem to indi-
cate, 'dementia praecox'.) This *modula* of 1909, through a
series of unknown, but surely providential circumstances,
is later to find its way into the records of the High Court
in Florence. Without a shadow of doubt it is the most
important surviving document about the poet.

COMMUNE OF MARRADI

Information module
regarding the admission of patients into the Florence Insane
Asylum

Patient: Campana Dino

Personal details

Surname and name of patient	Dino Campana
Age profession	23 years – Student
Whether poor or well-to-do	Well-to-do
Place of birth	Marradi
Domicile	Marradi (province of Florence)
Parents	Giovanni – Primary-school teacher
	Luti Francesca – housewife
	single

Case history

Moral character prior to madness, habits and usual occu-	The patient is most studious; knows several languages

pations.

| | and is registered for 3rd year Chemistry. Has a quick and lively mind. |

Whether there is or has been insanity among the patient's relatives, and, if so, which.	An uncle of the patient's died in an Asylum.
Whether the patient has been previously subject to insanity or any other disorder.	The patient has previously been admitted to the Imola asylum.
Physical and moral causes.	Heredity – Alcoholism
Period and mode of development of madness, and whether intermittent or continuous.	During the period since he left the Imola Asylum he has at intervals repeatedly shown signs of madness.
Present symptoms of madness, whether physical or psychic.	The patient is extremely untidy both at home and in public, to the point of attracting the attention of children meeting him in the street. He has a particular loathing for his mother, who has had to leave home. He is especially dangerous after he has imbibed to excess. He has repeatedly threatened various persons, both in public places and on the public way.
Practical treatment.	
Diagnosis of the form of madness and, if possible, of its nature.	Dementia praecox??
Statement of the reasons why the doctor undersigned deems	He is dangerous to members of his family and to others.

*it necessary to confine and
treat the patient in an Asylum.*

Signature of doctor

Marradi, 9 April 1909   Dr Augusto Pellegrini

'Wait. Let me at least drink my coffee,' Dino pleads as he leaves Dr Pellegrini's surgery. But the lance-corporal is unyielding. 'We must catch the ten o'clock train.' They go up the steps to the Town Hall and enter the mayor's office, where the typist hands the *carabinieri* the temporary admission order 'into the Florence Asylum as a measure of Public Safety' for 'Campana Dino son of Giovanni aged 23, single': 'highly dangerous, insofar as during the hours of darkness he has threatened peaceable citizens'.

However irregular (both by logic and by law, a 'lunatic' who has not been released from the Imola asylum cannot be kept under observation in the Florence asylum), the matter is swiftly implemented. On 10 April 1909 the director of the San Salvi asylum, Professor Rossi, informs the Procurator Royal that among those admitted is one 'Campana Dino son of Giovanni, aged 23 – single – born and dom.d in Marradi – well-to-do'. 'I hereby notify Yr. Excellency,' he writes, 'that on the 9th instant the patient named herein, from Marradi, has been admitted to this Institution by provisional authority of the Mayor's order of 9th inst..' Professor Rossi (whose first name does not appear on the documents) again writes to the Procurator Royal concerning Dino Campana on 22 April 1909: 'I hereby inform Yr. Excellency that the person named herein is ineligible for membership of the Asylum. I therefore request authority to release him.' In pursuance of this request, the Procurator Royal (whose signature to this document is unfortunately illegible), writes to the president of the Florence High Court asking him 'to order the release of Campana Dino'. The President (Ceglini? This is another illegible signature) accepts the request of the Procurator Illegible on 24 April 1909, 'having seen the papers regarding Campana Dino's mental state' and 'having seen the Dr's conclusions dated 22.4.1909'. He therefore orders that 'the person named' be instantly released: and he does not realize, does not know, that his decision has created the precedent – highly interesting from the juridical point of view and from the clinical point of view – of a 'seriously psychopathic' patient whose 'prospects of recovery are extremely problematical' on one side of the Apennines who is not a patient on the other side...

Dino returns to freedom. He hasn't got a cent and he is certainly not keen to rejoin those who sent him to the madhouse. So he goes to spend a few days at the house of that uncle Francesco Campana, sub-Procurator Royal at the Florence High Court whom Marradian memory characterizes as an 'original', 'zestful' person: not mad exactly, but 'a bit odd'. Is it unfair to imagine that Francesco paid his brothers back in the same coin, regarding them as gentlemen, but limited in outlook by the small horizons of Marradi? Of the three brothers Campana he is certainly the only one who has a clear view of his nephew's legal situation: and in all probability it is he who intercedes in the present case with the schoolmaster Giovanni to make him see reason and adopt a gentler policy towards his son. I imagine, therefore, that the day after Dino's arrival Francesco writes to his brother: 'Dear Giovanni. This is to let you know that yesterday, 24th inst., Dino was released from the San Salvi hospital as being ineligible, that is, the doctors have not judged him to be mad. He's at home with me now and has expressed the desire to stay a few days. He's told me about his American adventure and has also spoken to me about the Marradi people's hostility towards him. From what he says, he is the object of out-and-out persecution: and in that he is certainly exaggerating. Allow me nevertheless to tell you with my usual frankness what I think about this lad of yours and ours and about his troubled history. Dino is naturally quiet, reflective, sensitive; also a bit touchy, I know. Like all sensitive people and like all our family. He is not mad: but he certainly will become so if you persist in making him do things for which he has no inclination and in thwarting him at every turn. You already know what my ideas are. Temperamentally I would say that he is closer to the artistic than to the military or the scientific, and as for sending him to America allow me to say that that idea seemed to me from the first to be far-fetched, if not actually harebrained. Sure. it's an ill wind that blows no good and it's good for today's young people to travel the world a bit. He seems to have learnt some English and some Spanish in America, so one might say that he has a grounding in four foreign languages. He's a clever lad in his own way and if I write all this to you it's because it makes my heart bleed to see him abandoned among the insane when all his problems might possibly be smoothed out with a little understanding... If I've spoken out of turn, forgive me. If on the other hand you think you could make use of me for the lad's future, command and I will obey. Greetings to Fanny and Manlio. Your most affectionate Francesco.'

Back in Marradi in mid-May, Dino is the village idiot as he was in April when he was led off under guard; but in many respects the situation has changed. First of all, his relation with his father is different. The latter no longer tries to plan the future for him but, on the contrary asks Dino what he would like to do, 'in the arts, for example'. (Discarding only poetry, which 'no one can live on'.) His relations with the Marradi worthies have also changed. Those gentlemen have come out of the business looking foolish, and rather diminished. (People think: 'If they can't even manage to get the village idiot put away, what kind of town worthies are they?') Imperceptibly, Dino's relationship with his mother has changed, too: and this is the most important change. Taciturn and shrewish as ever, Fanny divides her time between religious and domestic functions but behaves less aggressively towards Dino, appears almost resigned to accepting his existence. A kind of weary forbearance is slowly beginning to take the place of her fury of the preceding years; and the process is of course gradual, almost imperceptible; there are still rows in the Campana household, dishes are still smashed: but less and less frequently, and also with less violence than in the past. Mother and son confront each other *'comme deux ennemis rompus / que leur haine ne soutient plus / et qui laisse tomber leurs armes'*. ('Like two exhausted enemies / whom hatred, though still unappeased, / sustains no more, they drop their swords': lines from *Canti Orfici*, written between 1910 and 1913.)

What grows irresistibly, on the other hand, is Dino's reputation as a 'madman' in Marradi, and with it his persecution by the street-urchins and those who while away their time at the café, Dino's 'normal' contemporaries. These take as their acclaimed model, at this time, the extremely young town clerk, Bucivini Capecchi. (Entrepreneurial in his dealings with women, ambitious, businesslike, astute.) This Bucivini Capecchi, whom Zavoli interviews when in his sixties, figures in Dino's nightmares even when he's far from Marradi: in Bologna, in Florence, in Genoa. 'Then I met someone from my town,' we read in the first draft of a piece in the *Canti Orfici*, 'and I can still hear the calls of the jackals waiting for me there. Did you in the hour of terrible anguish hear the crowd chant Barabbas Barabbas: did you see Barabbas gaze upon you with the contempt of your own town clerk? Truly I cannot take my life without being a coward. And besides by this time . . .'

For two or three successive summers from 1909 Dino frequents the 'workshop' of master Michele Cordigiani, a painter and artist of Marradi. He makes some copies in plaster, practises with charcoal, water-colours, clay. Mostly, he talks art and literature with Michele's son, Edoardo: he has lived many years in France, has been a pupil of Renoir and Cézanne and now has a studio in Florence and only reappears in Marradi during the summer. Edoardo Cordigiani talks to him about the writers and poets whom he's met: Mallarmé, Gide, Maeterlinck, Jacob, Apollinaire... He lends Dino books which the latter eagerly reads up in his mountains, at Campigno or at the Hermit's Pass. One Leonardo Zaccarini, old Michele's young assistant, wants to join him on his long walks: he walks along beside him, he persists. If only to shake him off, Dino doesn't hesitate to exploit his own reputation as a madman: 'Don't come along with me, Zaccarini. It won't do you any good to be with me. I'm mad.'

In October he goes to stay at his uncle Francesco's house in Florence until the following June. He follows French and German courses at a private school, goes to the theatre with his friend Francini (a young Marradian working as a cub journalist for the daily *La Nazione*, who writes plays), haunts artists' studios: Gordigiani's, Costetti's, Pettoruti's, Candia's... He sends letters to newspapers and journals offering to contribute literary or theatre criticism. One of these missives has survived and has been published. Dino

138

describes himself as an 'ex–University student, taking a dip-
loma in languages' and is applying to a Virgilio Scattolini,
editor of the obscure weekly, *Difesa dell'Arte* (The Defence
of Art). 'I know five languages,' says Dino, 'and I gladly
offer myself to transfuse a little young blood into the veins
of this old Italy, and that goes for any question which you
feel it is appropriate to raise. I too possess some genuinely
and vitally modern culture and thinking. And my distant
travels and the diverse manifestations of human genius
which I have studied in diverse modern literatures have
imparted to me a certain breadth, serenity and independence
of judgement.'

News of the end of the world appears in the Italian newspapers at the beginning of 1910 and there and then no one heeds it, it is taken as readership bait, an impromptu gimmick by journalists with nothing to report... 'Whatever can they think up next, after this?' Little by little, though, as articles, interviews, diagrams pile up, people begin to realize that this is no fantasy or long-range prophecy: it's serious scientific stuff. There is no doubt about it, say the astronomers. During the night between 18 and 19 May planet Earth will pass through the tail of Halley's Comet, which is composed of rare and poisonous gases: instantaneously, every life form inhabiting it will perish. Men and beasts will lie, according to the letter of the ancient Scriptures, like dung spread on the field. The views of physicists, chemists, mathematicians are sought: There is no error in the calculations, the event – they say – is ineluctable. On both sides of the ocean the declarations by the celebrated astronomer Flammarion about the 'impending catastrophe' achieve particular prominence. Panic sweeps the world. The number of suicides – this is incredible, but true – increases with the approach of the fateful appointment with the Comet, fixed for 3.20 a.m. on Thursday 19 May. On Wednesday the 18th, the eve of annihilation, the daily *La Nazione* exhorts the Florentines to repent and commend their souls to God in words which might not have displeased Fra Girolamo Savonarola: 'Let us therefore make our examination of conscience,' urges the anonymous leader-writer, 'and ask God's forgiveness for our innumerable sins: tomorrow, or the day after, we will be no more.' Right from early evening the entire population is out on the streets. The churches have opened their doors and are overflowing with people who press in from all around. The Arno embankments are unbelievably crowded; nobody, however old or ill, can bear the thought of dying alone. From time to time shots ring out in the streets or alleys of the town centre, there are brief chases, furious fights: the newspapers of Thursday the 19th, all of which appear in the afternoon or evening, speak of dozens of arrests, of an open, head-on clash between the police and the criminal underworld, which has fully mobilized itself to loot apartments and goldsmiths' shops... Crimes are carried out in the certainty that they will go unpunished. In Bagno a Ripoli a young man of twenty-three batters his step-father to death; in Via Valfonda, alongside the station, a man's body is found – the circumstances of his death are unclear. Bands of drunkards roam the streets singing obscenities to the tune of the *Miserere*, the *De Profundis*, the *Dies irae*, the same hymns which the faithful are singing in the churches. Spontaneous torchlight processions ascend the slope to the Piazzale Michelangelo, Dino among them, amid masked people in fancy-dress dancing the polka or the can-can, keeping time with all sorts of instruments: accordions, clackers, tin cans... 'See them here, the tellers of this Savings Bank which is the world. Parleying with the Eternal Father over their own death or turning it into a feast, with this absurd gaiety: because death is wastage and because wastage, for them, is not something to be taken seriously. Ever.'

From the shrubs flanking the avenues come the moanings and pantings of perfunctory copulations. The sky teems with stars: where should the Comet be? 'Piazzale Michelangelo,' the reporter for *La Nazione* jots down on his pad, 'is awash with people who are intoxicated with a carnival-like elation as they gaily wait to greet the Comet fair with streaming hair.' 'Piazzale Michelangelo is choked with motor-cars, bicycles, motor-cycles and carriages which have carried hundreds and thousands of persons up here.' Alas, the appointed time goes by without the Comet making its appearance to wipe out the human race; people seem 'disappointed'. 'At 3.20 the expectations of the numerous viewers were disappointed, because the Comet did not appear.' 'As the first glimmerings appear in the East, Venus gleams in a marvellous half-light as on a nacreous conch, alive with glintings of light.' 'The Comet hasn't appeared! The crowd streams down through the gardens and the flowered stairways.'

The summers of 1910 and 1911 bring no change. Dino roams the mountains, visits old Gordigiani's workshop, helps his friend Francini to stage two plays (*'Trudger' in the Limelight*, 1910; *The Scrapbook*, 1911) for Marradi's little theatre. Dino acts in both: he is solo Chorus in the first and in the second plays the Pedagogue, caricaturing his father, who (according to local memory) hugely enjoys the show. This appearance of normality, however, is set against a milieu – Marradi – that misses no opportunity of mocking and baiting its 'madman'; which cannot do without a 'madman' because television has not yet been invented and there is not much entertainment... (When Sergio Zavoli comes to Marradi, in the early Fifties, he encounters, in essence, three kinds of reaction among those who remember the 'madman': 'Amazement on receiving confirmation of public interest in Dino Campana; inability to square today's esteem with the memory of past discredit; fear of having no fitting memory of their fellow-townsman, with apologies for having wretchedly mistaken him for a lunatic and nothing else. They were so apologetic that they outdid one another in citing evidence of the lunacy that was finally being honoured.')

Early in the morning of 15 September 1910 Dino sets out from Marradi on foot to climb that mountain, La Verna, where, almost seven hundred years earlier, another lunatic like himself – Francis – was reduced to living for three months with 'brother' wolf and 'sister' eagle, sleeping on

the bare rock and living on berries and roots. But La Verna
is not within easy reach, and Dino's journey (a round trip
of over two weeks) turns into a veritable pilgrimage over
mountain passes and stony paths, in the 'mystic solitude',
in the 'mystic silence' of 'barbaric valleys' and 'timeless
forests'. In that silence and in that solitude Dino reflects
upon his own poetry as a 'poetry of movement and a Tuscan
poetry', he reconnoitres its antecedents. The poetry of
movement is in Dante ('Dante his poetry of movement, I
recall it all. O pilgrim, o pilgrims walking full of thought.')
Tuscan poetry reveals itself fully in the 'divine primitives':
Leonardo, Andrea del Castagno, Francis. Walking beneath
the bright sky 'within space, outside time', the twenty-five-
year-old Dino Campana decides his future: he will be a poet
and nothing else. (As Francis became a saint; as Andrea del
Castagno became a painter.) He will restore life and harmony to 'the Tuscan poetry that has been'.

The itinerary of his journey is given in the prose account
in the *Canti Orfici* and in the 'lost' manuscript: Campigno,
the Scalelle Pass, Castagno d'Andrea ('A plaque to Andrea
del Castagno in the presbytery'), Falterona, Campigna ('not
Campigno'), Stia, La Verna 'fortress of the spirit, the huge
rocks piled up heavenwards by a violent law, pacified first
by nature that had clothed them in green forests, then
purified by a spirit of infinite love...'

His journey back is a farewell to childhood which for the
poet ends only here and only now. At the wall of La Verna
where Francesca's inscription reminds him of a distant
'yearning'. ('I walked off through the forest feeling over
again that first yearning. I recalled her victorious eyes, the
line of her brow: perhaps she had never known: and now
I rediscovered her at the end of my pilgrimage breaking
into such sweet confusion, up there far away from everything.') Or in the Campigno valley: 'I see a boy once more,
the same boy, lying down there on the grass. He seems to
be asleep. I recall my own boyhood: how long it is since
the magnetic gleamings of the stars first told me of the

infinities of deaths!... Time has passed, has gathered, has passed: just as the water flows past, motionless to that boy: leaving behind it silence, the profound, changeless pool: preserving silence as every day its shadow...'

Returning from La Verna at the beginning of October, Dino does not go down to Marradi, among the 'howling jackals', but stops in Campigno, where a widow lets him a room in her house for a month. He reads, writes, roams around undisturbed in the silence and the peace of the forest. 'I've landed among good folk. My bedroom window facing the winds and a widow once housekeeper in command of a Romagnol nobleman, her boy a poor little bird with gentle features and a hesitant soul, a poor little bird dragging along a broken leg and the wind battering at the window from the cloud-laden horizon, the mountains distant, high, the monotonous growl of the wind. Far away, snow has fallen.

'The lady housekeeper, silent, makes up my bed and the housemaid helps her.

'Monotonous lovable patriarchal life.'

According to Marradian legend as recorded by Gerola and divulgated by Falqui, it is precisely at this time that Dino, prowling over the mountains, begins to pull off exploits even more audacious than those of his fellow-countryman Stefano Pelloni, known as 'il Passatore', who used to terrify people with a blunderbuss. Armed only with his reputation as a madman, he moves into ploughmen's houses: he compels them to lay out meals for him, to make his bed, to clean his room for weeks and months on end and all this purely through terror of his 'possible reactions'...
The truth is less epic than that, and can be gauged on the basis that Marradi, Palazzuolo sul Senio, Campigno and the

whole Mugello area at the beginning of the century are country holiday resorts: 'agri-tourist centres', they would be called today. Dino does not intrude into anybody's house but applies to people who regularly let out rooms; he bargains over the rent – usually very modest – and stays there for the agreed period: a fortnight or a month. If he has the money, he pays his own way; if he hasn't, he sends for some to his father, who does nothing to discourage these 'holidays' of his son's, and in all likelihood himself suggested the idea. Dino's reputation as a madman is now such that the guardians of law and order fear possible incidents. It was quite possibly the new mayor of Marradi himself, the engineer Vincenzo Mughini, who in friendly wise counselled Giovanni to keep 'that lad' as far away from Marradi as possible: 'Seeing that Marradi can't be kept away from him.' Or else it is also possible that Captain Anonymous of the local *carabinieri* summoned Torquato Campana, the 'lunatic''s guardian, to tell him: 'I know the way these things go. One word too many, one glass too many, and, God forbid...' – Who knows. Who knows if the Marradi authorities really intervened to warn the 'lunatic''s relatives of the hazards of the situation. I think they did, and that Giovanni's tolerance of Dino's 'holiday-makings' – between the autumn of 1910 and the summer of 1912 – is a token of civic, as well as domestic, virtues...

During the winter of 1910-11 Dino is in Florence again, following the same course in languages as the previous year, which he is never to complete. He meets a few writers: Ferdinando Agnoletti, a milkman; Ugo Tommei, a stationer's assistant and official confessor of the Florentine men of letters; Italo Tavolato, a student obsessed with the idea of writing for *La Voce* magazine. In the spring (April?) he begins to go to the University to hear the lectures of Professor Guido Mazzoni, foremost spokesman of the academic culture of the times. A scholar, rhetorician, poet, who inherited and carried on Carducci's 'historical criticism', this illustrious Mazzoni holds the Chair of Italian Literature at the University of Florence, is president of the Accademia della Crusca (custodian of the Italian language), honorary member of the august Accademia dei Lincei and Senator of the Realm, nominated by His Majesty on 26 January 1910 along with the philosopher Benedetto Croce and few other eminent men of learning. But for the young Campana he is above all the pupil of Carducci, – indeed, his favourite pupil: and his lectures of 1910–11 are of interest to Dino because they conclude the course on nineteenth-century Italian poetry by discussing the Bard himself. Even physically, the 'Professor and Senator' appears 'venerable' to Dino. Mazzoni is tall and austere-looking, his hair, already snow-white, close-cropped, 'King Umberto' style; with a great chestnut-coloured moustache. He wears stiff collars and bow-ties after the fashion of the previous century. He is over-suspicious and touchy, with a weakness for calling in the police over every trifle: but of this Dino is unaware. What he does know is that he is an outsider, not registered for the course and not entitled to attend the lectures: so he keeps himself to himself, tries to be invisible and ends up by being far more conspicuous than if he were in full view. Mazzoni, noticing him, asks his assistants: 'What's that shaggy creature?' 'Where's he from?' 'Who is he?' The attendants are consulted. They say: 'He's never been seen until the start of this month.' Some remark on the stranger's appearance: his countryman's jacket, his blackened fingernails, his short russet beard. 'What if he's an anarchist?' Mazzoni blenches, aghast: 'An anarchist attending my lectures!' 'If he comes again we'll ask to see his card,' an attendant stoutly volunteers. But the Professor is of quite a different mind: 'Heavens above. Don't speak to him. Don't even address him. He might be armed. He might...' He waves his hand to hint at disaster. 'As soon as he enters, summon the police. It's their job. Don't get yourselves involved. Good God... An anarchist, whatever next.'

A few days after this imaginary scene Dino Campana from Marradi, aged twenty-five, unmarried, well-to-do, is 'captured' by the police just outside the University, handcuffed and hauled into the police van which then carries him to police headquarters: where he is subjected to a 'thorough' search – which includes his clothes and his orifices – and protracted interrogation, a prelude to Pariani's cross-questionings. The details which the police pursue most eagerly are those concerning his travels undertaken without his family's knowledge – to Switzerland, France and Belgium – and his having studied chemistry. 'Now tell us about the bombs,' snaps his questioner at one stage, shining the lamp into his eyes. 'How many have you made, and who for?' Dino: 'But what are you on about... What bombs?' The inspector: 'Answer. We know all about you. We know you were studying chemistry to learn how to make explosives.' Dino: 'No, I couldn't do a thing.' 'I've only taken three exams.'

Thanks to the intervention of his uncle the magistrate, Dino does not land in gaol: but his arrest outside the University suggests that there is something we don't know about, some pre-existent police interest... Who can tell? Possibly Dino resembled one of the numerous subversives and anarchists wanted by the authorities all over Europe; perhaps, and more likely, he had met some anarchists and the police wanted to frighten him into collaborating and informing for them. After so many years, we can only speculate. The one thing we do know is that as soon as he is released Dino flees from Florence and stays away for two years. He spends a few days at his parents', then goes to live in Badia, in the house of a peasant called Pietro Donatini, who rents him a room. Here, in the silence of the countryside, he spends much of 1911 and of the following year. He goes to Bologna from time to time to buy books and see people, and there meets a friend of Francini's: Nicola Spano, secretary of the Faculty of Letters and an aspiring playwright. He frequents the Bar Nazionale and there meets his first biographer, the Bolognese, Bejor. He will meet his other biographer, Ravagli, a little later, around the end of 1912...

The summer of 1911 brings a central event in the life of Dino Campana: he discovers love (venal) and woman (a prostitute). The *Canti Orfici* give richly detailed accounts. Initiation at the age of twenty-six is difficult for someone who has long been repressed and afflicted by juvenile complexes and who at his first encounter with sex assaulted

'Ophelia's corpse'. The month is 'torrid August'; the day, 'the longest day' in Dino's life, when his entire life so far comes to a head: 'Years and years and years melted in the triumphant sweetness of memory.' The place is the Faenza brothel, run, at this time, by 'an ancient and opulent Matron with the profile of a ram – her black hair wound supply around her barbarically adorned statuesque head'. This woman whiles away her time playing patience with Neapolitan playing-cards which are 'long and greasy'. The ceremony is performed in two stages or, if you prefer, is delayed by a momentary impediment on the part of the Priestess, who, at the novice's arrival, 'was sleeping with her mouth half-open, rasping in heavy slumber, her splendid supple ambered body half-naked'. The poet agrees to converse with the Matron Bawd; as they talk, the 'Priestess of barren pleasure' awakens, listens, and butts in. Though Dino strives to distance the whole scene in memory and dream, the recalcitrant fleshy matter emerges, strong and unquelled, not to be transfigured even by the mythological overtones. So what actually dominates is precisely the descriptive 'realism' which should have provided no more than the setting for the unveiling of the mystery: the sun, the sultriness, the plain of the Romagna, the empty villa, the two bored women who entertain their only client well beyond what market laws dictate; just to while away the time...

In fact, Dino Campana's encounter with the Faenza 'hand-maid' is only a prelude to that with the 'white colossal prostitutes' ('the Mothers') who first appear to him arrayed along the Genoa waterfront in February 1912. (The date is certain. We know from a note of Dino's that in 1912, in February, he stayed in Genoa for a few days or a few weeks. We also know his address: 27, Vico Vegetti, apartment 2.) 'Shaded by the green streetlamps the white colossal prostitutes dreamed vague dreams by the weird light in the wind. The sea mixed into the wind its salt which the wind mixed and lifted into the lust-smell of the alleys – and the white Mediterranean night played with the enormous white shapes of the females amid the flames' weird efforts to tear themselves out of the lamps' hollows. The women watched the flame and sang songs of hearts in chains. All the preludes had fallen silent now. Night, night's quieter joy had descended now. The Moorish doorways were laden and entwined with monstrous black portents whilst the dark blue backdrop grew embosomed with stars. Solitary now night reigned enthroned ablaze teeming with all its stars and flames. Ahead, like a monstrous gash, plunged a street. Alongside doors' angles, white caryatids of an artificial firmament dreamed their faces resting on their palms. The pure imperial line of her profile and neck was lit with opaline splendour. With a swift gesture of imperial youth she drew her light garment over her shoulders in readiness and her window glittered in expectation until gently the shutters closed on a twofold shadow. And my heart was entranced with dream, for her, for her evanescent as evanescent love, the bestower of love in seaports, the caryatid of firmaments of fortune. Upon her divine knees, upon her shape as pale as a dream issuing from among the innumerable dreams of the shadow, among the innumerable delusive lights, the ancient friend, the eternal Chimaera held in her red hands my ancient heart.'

The 'pale shape', 'evanescent'...In Genoa, in 1912, an invisible murderess enters the blood of the poet like 'a dream issuing from among the innumerable dreams of the shadow'; a dream melancholy and 'vain'. ('Everything is vain, vain is the dream: everything is vain, everything is dream: Love, spring-time of dream it's you alone, it's you alone appearing in the veil of violet fumes. Like a white cloud, like a white cloud next to my heart, oh stay oh stay oh stay! Don't grieve o Sun!') And love, 'eternal Chimaera', enters, as so often, into wedlock with death: 'Faces, faces eyes smiled at from the brink of dreams, you young charioteeresses upon the weightless ways of dream whom I garlanded in fervour: o fragile verses, o garlands of deep night's loves...From the garden a song falters into a feeble chain of sobs: the vein is open: arid and red and sweet is the skeletal panorama of the world.'

In the spring of 1912 Dino is in Badia, in his mountains: he ponders, reads, composes the prose and verse of the book which he had planned to write in Paris. He doesn't feel quite right, but doesn't attach too much importance to the fact. Probably he does not realize he has the clap until the beginning of June and probably also, rather than try a doctor in Marradi, he hurries over to Faenza or Bologna to see a specialist in venereal diseases. We can imagine the scene ('Undress', 'Raise your arms', 'Lower them', 'Walk', 'Get dressed'), a trying one for Dino. We can imagine the medicines prescribed (mercury-based ointments and powders) and the absolute prohibition against intimate relations with any other person 'for at least one year'. (Such a prohibition would, by the way, explain Dino's dogged chastity – attested by Ravagli – during the autumn of 1912 and the following winter: 'For certain not once, on the stations of our collective peripatetic libertinage, did he condescend to sacrifice to Venus Pandemia.' 'He tagged along passively, without enthusiasm, saying little: he did not join in our perambulatory cavortings, our choruses of approach. In the parlour he would sit apart in a corner, as if to avoid the women's gaze . . .' 'At times, left to himself to muse in peace, he would suddenly laugh – a superficial laugh, though, brief and controlled: or he'd mumble incomprehensible cadences: or he'd look on, without letting it show, from beneath his brow . . .')

In July, Dino is ill, his body covered in blotches the size

of a one-lira piece. In August he goes down to Marradi and his father delivers a speech to him: not a sermon nor a rebuke: a speech. He says to him, Dino, you know what these white hairs of mine signify? They signify that I am almost sixty-five and that, barring deferments or special appointments, I'm close to retiring. How am I going to support you, and then who will support you when I'm gone? He says: 'Wake up, Dino. People can't live on dreams and people can't live on poetry. Even D'Annunzio hasn't managed it. His dogs have been sold off, his lecterns, his inkstands, if he hadn't taken his underwear and his socks with him to France they'd have been auctioned off too...' He extracts a letter from his pocket. He says: 'I've taken the liberty of writing to your friend Nicola Spano in Bologna; I hope you won't hold it against me. I've asked him to secure from the science faculty the information relating to an ex-student like yourself. How many examination sessions would be needed, if you re-registered this November, to obtain your degree.' 'His reply is...' – the schoolmaster puts on his glasses and unfolds the letter – 'his reply is that if you start on your dissertation right away and if in February you get through the physics examination which you ploughed, you could graduate in July 1914.' He folds up the letter, returns it to his pocket; he removes his presbyopic's glasses and puts them back in their case. He says: 'It's up to you to decide on what to do. If you want to complete your studies, this is the last chance I'm giving you, because after July 1914 you won't see another penny of mine.'

'He looked a few years older than us. Stocky, almost fair, of medium height, going by appearances you'd take him for a trader, an eccentric trader, doing poorly. Barmaids, waiters, strangers viewed him with covert mirth. He had long, copper-coloured hair, thick and curly, which framed a portrait of health: a small moustache that came to an end at the corners of his mouth and a small, economical beard that never grew far out from his chin.'

This is how, Ravagli says, Dino Campana strikes the Bologna students who frequent the Bar Nazionale towards the turn of 1912. University records show that he renews his registration on 22 November and that he repeats his physics examination with an excellent result: 27 out of 30. There is direct evidence about how he pursues his studies. 'I recall', says a chemistry graduate called Lina Mondini, 'that during the academic year 1912-13 Campana in part followed the course in quantitative chemical analysis, which was taught by Professor Scagliarini. His odd appearance, his peculiar personality, excited amused curiosity among the female students. And concern, too, in fact: for acids and superheated substances were used in the laboratory. Campana participated in all the experiments involved in the course, including, of course, the furnace-bellows – an apparatus which produces temperatures over 1000°C. But his behaviour was always normal and correct, perfectly correct. Suddenly, he disappeared: and none of us ever heard of him again.'

The 8th of December 1912, sees Dino's maiden publication. *Il Papiro* ('Nobilis charta universitaria: twenty *centesimi*') carries three unsigned pieces by him: 'La Chimera', 'Le cafard' and 'Dualismo'. (Since the publication of signed contributions is an honour reserved to graduates like the poet Stecchetti – actually, Olindo Guerrini – or the prose-writer Albertazzi and barred to students, Dino is officially bound to adopt a goliardic pseudonym for each piece, and produces three puns on his name Campana – 'Bell': 'Campanone' – 'Great Bell'; 'Campanula' – 'Bluebell'; 'Din-Don' – 'Ding-Dong'.)

Dino's friends and fellow-students at this time are Olindo Fabbri, Federico Ravagli, Mario Bejor, Quirico Dall'Oca, Bucci, Ughelli, Pianori... His closest friendship is that with Fabbri, who puts him up in his room on Via Castiglione when Dino is thrown out from Via Zamboni, and treats him very warmly: he gives him advice about his studies, drags him along on sophomore jaunts to taverns and bordellos, even jokes about his poetry... More at arm's length is Nicola Spano, that is, 'Judas, my best friend, on the University's administrative staff': whom Dino now suspects of being his father's informer, giving him a wide berth pending an outcome which is to be his own self-vindication. ('We'll settle our accounts,' says he.)

To entertain his fellow-students Dino Campana performs two exploits, which we will call respectively 'the chair stunt' and 'the dog stunt'. The chair stunt is easily described. Ravagli: 'One evening, returning from the *Eden*, we skirted the geometry of tables neatly arranged outside the Café dell'Arena on Piazza Garibaldi. Campana, without saying a word, picked up a chair: going along with us, imperturbable and deaf to our high-spirited remarks, carried it all the way to Piazza Nettuno, where, to the helpless mirth of the onlookers, he hoisted it atop the Giant.'

The dog stunt, on the other hand, is one of the main supports on which the 'Campana legend' stands. Going from mouth to mouth and from page to page, the incident has split into two, four, ten separate events occurring in different places and in the presence of innumerable witnesses: it has swollen into a record of Western-style brawls with premises devastated, shop-windows and signs smashed, armed threats...Luckily, a report in *Il Giornale del Mattino* enables us to reconstruct what actually happened. On the day after Christmas (26 December 1912) Dino dines with his friends. Towards four o'clock in the afternoon he rises from the table and, swaying slightly, heads towards 'his quarters in No. 52, Via Zamboni' accompanied by 'one Quirico Dall'Oca of No. 42, Via Mazzini, and one Paolo Bucci, living at No. 36, Via Cartoleria'. On the staircase inside the building they encounter 'a young valet employed by Prof. Gorrieri, who lives in No. 34 of the same street', leading on a leash a small dog wearing a little red coat with little bells. Without a word, Dino seizes the dog, lifts it over the banister and 'deposits' it on the floor below, arousing half a hullabaloo: yelps, shrieks from a girl coming up the stairs, abuse from the valet. The latter, however, is put to flight and pursued into the café on the ground floor . . . Here, Ravagli says, Dino Campana performs deeds worthy of the hero of Ariosto's *Orlando Furioso*: 'He bursts into the café under the arcade – where the chemist's shop now is – where the girl [*sic*] had taken refuge. Here he set about overturning tables, swinging chairs about, smashing glasses and bottles in insane fury. The café proprietor and the few alarmed customers vainly tried to cool his wrath.' The reporter of *Il Giornale del Mattino*, on the other hand, only says that in the café Dino receives a few punches and clears out. That would be the end of it if the commander of the town watch in person didn't happen to be walking along the street. 'Yesterday afternoon, towards 16.00 hours, the commander of the town watch, Dalmonte-Casoni, was proceeding along Via Zamboni accompanied by some members of his family when, near house No. 52, the noise of a glass door slamming caught his attention and he saw a young man, hatless, who, freeing himself from the grip of a group of people standing at the entrance of the café which is situated in that building, raced off towards the municipal theatre. Imagining he was a thief, Dalmonte-Casoni pursued him and caught up with him near Via del Guasto.' Dino, not comprehending why a stranger should show such determination, tells him to 'clear off' and threatens him: first with a 'cobble-stone which he found on the ground', then with a key. 'Fortunately,' concludes the anonymous reporter, 'a few minutes later Pagani Enrico, Sparragni Carlo and Lucchetti Aldo of the town watch turned up and helped their captain to disable the young man, who seemed possessed of a veritable frenzy, and take him by vehicle to the town hall guardroom. Here, Dr Gregorini, who examined him, found evidence of a disorder

and had him taken to the Ospedale Maggiore. The young
man is the student Campana Dino son of Giovanni, aged
28, from Marradi, enrolled at our University.'

Following this episode of the dog, which highlights two things – Commander Dalmonte-Casoni's heroism and Dino's lucklessness – the latter is thrown out of his lodgings in Via Zamboni and summoned to police headquarters, where he is received like an old acquaintance and made to talk about himself. ('Why have you resumed your studies?' 'Why are you back in Bologna?' 'Why were you arrested in Florence?') As ever, when he's involved with the police, Dino would like to get away at once, right away: but Fabbri, Spano, Dall'Oca manage to dissuade him from interrupting his studies: 'Take the physics exam you've prepared for, at least,' they urge him. 'Then if you really must clear out, you can ask for a transfer to another University. What's the sense of dropping everything? You haven't killed anyone.' Dino decides: he'll go to Genoa. The police there, he says, have other things to think about than persecuting penniless students as the lot here in Bologna do. ('Bologna! A town of bigots and pimps, never a murder, never any crime of blood!') He carries on attending the course throughout January: though exasperated by the attitude of the inspector ('the classical, bewhiskered, colossal emissary') and of the constables who wink at him when they come across him in the street and smirk as if to say: 'We know each other, you and I!' At the beginning of February he gets through his physics examination and goes off to Genoa; on the 24th of that month he secures his transfer from one University to another. On 3 March 1913 Nicola Spano ('Judas') writes of him to his father the schoolmaster: Some friends in that town have seen him, and he seems to be all right there. He's started attending laboratory sessions and lectures, but no one can vouch for his persevering in those studies. He needs to be encouraged, weaned from idle ways, made to complete his course. He could graduate in July 1914 and then work as a pharmacist, begin to earn some money...'

Dino Campana, pharmacist... In the spring of 1913, Genoa 'sings, laughs, varies in iron its fecund seaward-thrusting symphony'; and he immediately forgets his chemistry and his father's concern, renews his resolve to be 'a poet and nothing more'; to 'live, however meagrely, on poetry'. But to achieve that, he needs to get into print: and he applies to the literary journals as a smoker tries a tobacconist or a traveller the railways, without beseechings or adulations or professions of faith. On the contrary, his offerings of verse or prose pieces are accompanied by letters saying: 'Your journal is monotonous, very monotonous: the inevitable Palazzeschi, the obligatory Soffici.' '*Lacerba* is a reforming journal! In fact it's the perfect catalogue of the commandments of the Anti-Christ' (to *Lacerba*). 'I've established that to produce something readable a man's got to be thrashed till he's bleeding. I'd gladly do as much for nearly all the writers of *La Voce*' (to *La Voce*). Dino's attitude towards writer-publishers and in general those he calls the parvenus of literature is direct and unequivocal, utterly contemptuous of the rules of the literary game which are chameleon-like adaptability, servility, fitting in with the milieu. On their side, after their initial bewilderment, the parties concerned react by waging against the 'lunatic' a war which, in at least two cases (Papini and Palazzeschi), engenders acts of antagonism long after Dino's death, in the attempt to scotch his fame, annul his memory...

In Genoa, in the spring of 1913, Dino feels himself to be a

Futurist. He dreams of a day in which, over 'this land of the falsely youthful' which is Italy, 'a new firmament, a pure firmament' may shine, 'a metallic firmament burning with vertigo', 'a firmament where / friars and poets have not made their den like worms'. On Tuesday, 6 May, he watches the finish of the first leg (Milan-Turin-Genoa) of the fifth Giro d'Italia cycle race; hemmed in by the press of people thronging both sides of the Bisagno, he catches a glimpse of Girardengo, Canepari, Bordin, Pavesi, Ganna. He writes a poem ('Traguardo' – Finishing-line) dedicated to Filippo Tomaso Marinetti and mails it to the office of the Futurist Movement in Milan (No 61, Corso Venezia) along with three or four other unpublished pieces and a covering letter which mentions an almost-completed book, which would be happy to appear under the imprint of the Edizioni Futuriste di Poesia... But Marinetti, Dino will later relate, 'turned down the idea, who knows why'; and here we must pause to clear up another episode in the 'Campana legend', the one about Dino selling the *Canti Orfici* to the customers at the Giubbe Rosse (the Florence literary café) but, before handing over the copy, eyeing the purchaser's physiognomy, then ripping out a page here and there... 'Anyway,' he says, 'you wouldn't understand these bits.'

Those pages ripped out... Everybody has seen Dino ripping out pages: Papini, Soffici, Viviani, Binazzi, the Signorina Rivola whom Zavoli interviewed: People came by train all the way from Marradi to witness that miraculous salesmanship! Only, when they get down to business, every single person without exception has a sound copy and every single person mentions just one name – Marinetti. So Marinetti is the only person who can fairly reliably be said to have received a copy of the *Canti Orfici* with some pages missing. How many? Papini says 'nearly all'; Viviani, 'some'; yet another person says he gave him 'only the dust-jacket'... In reality, Dino's gesture has only one explanation: upon a proud impulse he wanted to remind Marinetti of his hasty and groundless rejection. He meant, more or less: 'You didn't care for these poems in manuscript, so you couldn't care for them in print either. In which case, I may as well remove them.'

Dino attends University only to listen to Alfredo Galletti's lectures on European culture (and in particular on Dante's poetry) as the outcome of the clash between its two 'souls' or 'ideas', the 'Latin idea' and the 'Germanic idea'... But the direction he usually takes when he leaves his lodgings in the Sestiere di Pré is down to the arcades and the *scagni* of the Sottoripa waterfront, towards the rocks of La Foce and the seaward fortifications. One day he unexpectedly meets Regolo. 'The street was deserted in the afternoon glare. He was staring dazzle-eyed at the sea. That face, the roving eye! He turned round: we recognized one another instantly! We embraced. How are things? How are things? Holding my arm, he wanted us to go out into the countryside: then I decided him to go down to the seashore instead. Lying on the shingle beach, we carried on calmly exchanging experiences. He'd returned from America. It all seemed natural and expected. Once more the devil had brought us together: for why? Light at heart, we didn't think of wondering. We talked and talked, until we clearly heard the sound of the waves breaking on the shingle of the beach. We raised our faces to the sun's crude light. The sea's surface was all dazzling. We had to eat. Let's go!'

As at Pavia and in Bahia Blanca, again in Genoa in 1913 Dino shares in Regolo's trade (receiving? contraband?). The two men roam the harbour area by night, enter the glittering dives, thronged with seamen of every race and nationality; plunge into the maze of 'sea-alleys'; go down to the water's edge again. They seek out business, adventure, love. From Sottoripa to the Bridge of the Thousand, the emporium-city of love arrays its Prostitute-Mothers against night's 'thousand-eyed devastation': and it is itself a gigantic female, it is 'the Octopus of Mediterranean nights', extending alleys and streets like tentacles, everywhere. Then everything happens suddenly. Regolo falls ill and disappears. The police search Dino's room and also subject him to an exhausting interrogation shining the electric light into his eyes: who are Regolo's accomplices? Where is Regolo? Who is he – Dino Campana? and what has he come to do in Genoa? ('Cut the bullshit, goldilocks. At the University they've never even heard of you.') Letters arrive from Marradi asking about exam results: browbeating him in the name of money, respectability, 'monstrous absurd reason'... A student from Olbia in Sardinia on his way back home for the summer invites him for a few days. Dino agrees, takes the boat: sees the island of La Maddalena, 'the white-cragged coast', the mountains of Aggius. Some images are imprinted in his memory and recur in his texts; but, overall, the trip is uneventful. By the end of July or the beginning of August Dino is back in Marradi: forced to repair to the hills so as to elude the enthusiasm of the townsfolk at having their 'madman' with them again... As he recounts to Cecchi in that letter of 13 March 1916 which is the final account of his life, the last testament of a man who is already being overtaken by the dark: 'Then I fled into my mountains, ever bestially persecuted and insulted, and in a few months wrote my Orphic songs including pieces already done. They were to be my life's justification because I was outside the law, before I *finished* dying *murdered* with the complicity of the government, in defiance of the *Statute*. Winter come, I went to Florence, to The Bitter [l'Acerba – *Lacerba*] to see Papini whom I knew by name.'

Dino's misadventures with the Florentine *littérateurs* begin in October of 1913, after he has rearranged and made a fair copy on 'pasta paper' (Rosai) of the verse and prose pieces he had assembled over ten years, leaving only the title in doubt: this appears on the left-hand side of the frontispiece as *The Longest Day*, and on the right-hand side as *And as pure spirit goes over the bridge*. Without a cent (his father hasn't given him any money since June), Dino makes it to Florence on foot, carrying only a small sack containing his manuscript and a few personal effects. His poverty is appalling. He walks barefoot to save his shoes, which he carries laced together over his left shoulder. He sleeps in the public shelter; he earns a few cents doing odd jobs as a messenger-boy or a porter. He offers his services to tourists to show them round Florence in their own language, but is turned down because of his appearance. At noon he eats at 'The Daily Bread Society'; in the evening he gets by, which generally means he goes without. Through Tommei or Tavolato he requests an interview with Papini and meets him at the Caffé Chinese by the old railway station. Papini turns up an hour late, quizzes him for a few minutes ('It transpired that he'd been round the world a good deal, more out of despair than for discovery, and that he had a fair knowledge of modern French poetry'), takes the manuscript which Dino gives him, and agrees without demur to return it the following day at Vallecchi's, the publisher in Via Nazionale: he has no intention of perusing it, anyway... It is only the character of Dino Campana that interests him, and he will say so in so many words: 'We, in those days, greatly preferred the crazy to the sane so we showed both him and his mangled prose a good face.'

On the following day – this is early in November – Papini returns the manuscript, saying to Dino – these are his exact words – that 'it's not quite what was expected but it's very very good', and inviting him to the *Lacerba* headquarters, that is, the Giubbe Rosse café in Piazza Vittorio Emanuele (the present Piazza della Repubblica). Dino goes there two or three times and realizes that he's entered a miracle-play where everyone acts an agreed role (his own, just by way of a change, being that of the madman) and everyone is waiting to get his work published in *Lacerba*, to become famous like Papini, like Soffici. To while away the time they go to the theatre to hiss 'passéist' plays or to Via Masaccio to mount lewd serenades beneath the windows of Senator Mazzoni (who mobilizes all the police forces in Florence against them). They posture, they caper, establish pecking order, prepare for their appointment with glory. They are 'the teenage literary mob', playing at literature: but Dino is dossing in the public shelter, has neither the time nor the desire to play games. He tackles Papini again and Papini says yes, sure, I see, but before I publish your work I must listen to Soffici, too. 'Bring me your manuscript again: I'll show it to Soffici.'

Two weeks go by. The weather in Florence is very cold (the newspapers mention sub-zero temperatures) and Dino is only wearing the between-season clothes which he brought in October. One morning, at Vallecchi's, Soffici finds himself face to face with a young man 'with down-turned eyes and hands red and swollen with chilblains hanging down by his sides'. Someone informs him that the strange visitor is Dino Campana (in fact: his cousin Dino Campana. Though the two men have never met before, they are both fully aware that they are second cousins. And so I should explain, before proceeding with my tale, that this Signor Ardengo Soffici – painter, poet, moralist and vice-Papini in the *Lacerba* days – is also besides, in all probability, the inventor and first publicist of the 'Campana legend' among the Florentine *littérateurs*. He is the only one who knows that Dino has been in a madhouse, that he has problems at home; and he, and nobody else, is the only person that Dino turns to in times of despondence, hoping for a word of fellow-feeling. For instance, he writes to him from Switzerland in 1915: '. . . you know I'm faced with the alternatives of the public shelter, hospital etc.'. – But when, forty years later, Soffici publishes that letter in the *Corriere d'Informazione*, he corrects that compromising expression, turns it into a tribute to his own experience of life and his own youthful bohemianism: '. . . You know the alternatives of the public shelter, the hospital etc.')

Haughty, and somewhat embarrassed, Soffici brushes off

the unexpected visitor ('I'm busy, as you see') and does not bestow upon him the honour of speaking to him until half an hour later, when he leaves the publisher's, with Dino trotting along beside him. He briefly answers Dino's questions ('No. Papini hasn't yet passed me your poems. I'll read them, rest assured') while observing that he's 'quivering like a leaf', that he's blowing on his hands and 'laughing nervously between one huff and the next'. (Talk about being crackers...) He scrutinizes his attire, of which he leaves to posterity this minute description: 'Without any kind of overcoat to protect him from that morning's intense cold, he wore a small hat resembling a saucepan, a light woollen nutbrown jacket, like the homespun ones worn by peasants and shepherds half a century ago, his feet swam in a pair of whacked-out down-at-heel shoes, while around his herculean legs flapped his skimpy trousers, made of an incredibly thin material, yellowish with pink and blue flowers, just like the muslin sheets used by country barbers on their customers and by housewives in poor families as curtains for their front windows.'

In reality, Ardengo Soffici has already received Dino's manuscript, along with a packet of mail for *Lacerba*: but both he and Papini have other things on their minds just now, at the end of November 1913, apart from reading and promoting Campana's poetry. They're mounting an exhibition of Futurist painters at Gonnelli's in Via Cavour; the *serata* with Marinetti at the Teatro Verdi in Florence; the *Lacerba* yearbook, to be entitled 'Almanacco purgativo': to mention only their main concerns. – But Dino, who has but one hope in life, is set on staying to see whether Soffici will read him. There's snow, and he signs up at the *Comune* as one of the shovellers to clear it, earning twenty or thirty lire which enable him to stay on a few more days. On the evening of 30 November he pays half a lira admission to see the Futurist exhibition: he sees Marinetti, Boccioni, Carrà; he examines the pictures hanging on the walls, but mostly he examines Soffici, tries hard to approach him and manage to speak to him. ('Perhaps he'll say something to me.') When he at last succeeds, Soffici shakes him off by introducing him to Prezzolini in such a way as to let the latter know whom he's dealing with. (A month later Dino writes to Prezzolini from Marradi: 'I'm the fellow who was introduced to you by Signor Soffici as a misfit at the Futurist exhibition.') Prezzolini, with his proverbial finesse, turns his back on him. Dino must feel discouraged; but a few days later he devises one last ruse to attract Soffici's attention. He'll write a poem on a painting which he saw displayed at Gonnelli's and whose title the catalogue gave as 'Pederasts' Tarantella'. (Just to shock the bourgeois.) A Futurist poem to tango to, which he personally will show to Soffici: 'Face, zigzag anatomy that darkens / The grim passion of an aged moon / Which gazes dangling from the ceiling / On a *café chantant* of a tavern / In America: the red swiftness / Of lights *tangoing on a tightrope / ashen Spaniard-girl / Hysterically in tango of lights expires:* / Which gazes in the *café chantant* / In America: / On the piano with fast hammer blows three / Little red flames have leapt free.'

The lines in italics are the ones to dance to: but Soffici is not to be found at the Giubbe Rosse and Dino is short of the half-lira needed to go in search of him at the exhibition. When he does at last find him, on Saturday 13 December, at the Buca dei Lapi trattoria, Soffici is with Marinetti and the others who are due to appear that same evening in the Verdi: Carrà, Boccioni, Cangiullo. The Futurists are dressed up to the nines – dark suits, stiff collars, bow-ties, gold cuff-links – and Soffici too sports a monocle most stylishly perched at his left eye. He says: 'What a pleasant surprise. The man from the woods. What fair wind...?' The Futurists regard Campana in puzzlement and also with some distaste on account of his 'louse-house', that is, his mane of hair and beard in the style of a nineteenth-century artist. 'Lord God in Heaven,' exclaims Boccioni, 'there are still people around with louse-houses.' 'I've been looking for you so as to give you a poem I've written about a painting of yours,' Dino says, addressing Soffici: it goes without saying that he feels awkward with all those eyes turned upon him. 'If it's not too great an imposition I'll read it to you now.' He takes the poem out of his pocket, but Soffici is quick to stop him: 'No thank you, Campana. You can see that we're planning this evening's performance. Buy yourself a ticket instead.' Carrà intervenes: 'You there, sir. Man of the woods. Have you got a goatskin?' Dino stares at him in dismay, and Carrà turns to Soffici and says: 'If he promises to come to the theatre wearing nothing but a goatskin we'll get him a complimentary ticket, won't we Soffici?' 'I also wanted to find out from you,' says Dino without paying any further attention to Carrà, 'about that bit of writing of mine that Papini passed on to you.' Soffici loses his temper: 'How many times must I tell you, Campana? I have nothing. Just check up. If you gave your poems to Papini, Papini must have them, damn it!' He flings his napkin down on the table. He turns to Marinetti, explains: 'Since we've been bringing out *Lacerba* I haven't even been able to have my meals in peace...'

Chilled and starving, Dino goes back to Marradi; and he's now almost convinced that the manuscript of his book is still in Papini's keeping. On 23 December 1913 he sends Papini a card with New Year greetings; signs 'the man of the woods' and asks to be remembered as such 'to Carrà and Soffici'. It is a last, emotional attempt at a friendly relationship; but Dino is already aware that he's been blackballed by that literary clique whose rules he has flouted and plans to get round the obstacle by going straight to the publishers: to Vallecchi, to Zanichelli, to Treves, to Rinfreschi... Someone – possibly Francini – advises him to send typed copies ('Otherwise', he tells him, 'it will go into the bin unread.') But the only typewriter in Marradi is the one belonging to the *Comune*. What's to be done? Dino appeals to his Uncle Torquato, who takes the matter up with the Mayor. 'Very well,' says engineer Mughini. 'During the week in between Christmas and New Year's day there's not much to do in the town hall. He can come along one of those days.' Word immediately goes round the town that the 'madman' has turned Futurist and wants to compose poems by typewriter so as to keep up with the times. 'He's using the typewriter in the town hall.' 'The Mayor's given his permission.' People expect who knows what to happen as a result of the 'madman''s intrusion into the stronghold of his persecutors, that is, the town clerk, Bucivini Capecchi, the deputy mayor, Ceroni... Mughini has had a word with them both, he's told them: 'I don't want any trouble. Understood?' One day at the end of 1913 Dino walks into the town hall without greeting anybody, goes and sits beside the typist and tells him: 'Write.' The typist makes all sorts of mistakes and Dino himself, for his part, forgets to make him take a carbon copy, so that a second sitting early in 1914 is necessary. (This trifling episode becomes the basis for an entire chapter of the 'Campana legend', the one regarding the re-writing of the manuscript 'mislaid' by Soffici. This re-writing – according to Bucivini Capecchi and Marradian legend – is carried out entirely in the town hall and interferes for months with the normal despatch of official business. Dino dashes around the offices terrorizing the clerks and especially tyrannizing the equivocal being in charge of the typewriter, who, the aforementioned Bucivini tells Gerola, was a woman and who, he then tells Zavoli, was a man. The conclusion of the legend is suggestive in its own way: the *Canti Orfici* were born in typescript in the Marradi town hall and are the product of the rough-and-ready but effective co-operation between the local officials and the poet. A pity that Bucivini Capecchi's version is belied by the covering note which, in May of the same year, Dino sends with his manuscript, ready for printing, to his friend Bandini. It says: 'I'm sending you the manuscript which I hope will be intelligible.')

The typewritten 'samples' of Campana's poetry leave the Marradi post office on 6 January 1914 in registered folders addressed to publishers Vallecchi in Florence, Zanichelli in Bologna, Treves in Milan and Rinfreschi in Piacenza. The attached letter, in identical copies to all four, reads: 'Distinguished Signor Vallecchi (Zanichelli, Treves, Rinfreschi). I am writing to you in the hope that you will take an interest in my case. I have enough narrative pieces and poems to make up a book and if you were willing to undertake publication I would dare to hope for a modest success. I have no money but I would guarantee immediate sale of fifty copies. Distinguished signor Vallecchi (Zanichelli, Treves, Rinfreschi), please help me. My humble respects, yours faithfully Dino Campana.'

During the first few days of 1914 Dino plans to go away, as soon as the winter becomes less harsh; to go and work in Switzerland and so earn the money to pay to have the book published, if a publisher does not come forward. The idea was suggested to him by *cavalier* Augusto Bandini, president of the Marradi Workers' Society and father of the Luigi Bandini ('Gigino') who is his dearest and most loyal friend. 'Here in Marradi we have Ravagli,' the *cavalier* Bandini tells Dino, 'who's a good typographer and also an associate of ours. He'll offer you favourable terms.' On 4 February Dino sends a note to Papini and Soffici politely but firmly asking them to 'leave my manuscripts, which I delivered to them, at the *Lacerba* office. A man is instructed to call for them on my behalf.' He packs his bag and leaves. In his pocket is a letter of introduction from the Marradi Workers' Society to the Berne Latin Union: this will see him across the border. At the Hospice at the frontier town of Domodossola he reads the inscription composed by the poet Pascoli in 1906 for the visit by the Queen of Italy, Margherita of Savoy: 'Let this stone declare – to Italian migrants on their journey – that on XXX October 1906 – here with the Holy Bishop and the united people – an August Lady came – the mother country visibly came to its border – weeping over all you suffer, blessing all you do – I have a great past and a great future – between the one and the other I have you working people – let me come with you and with you let me return.' Early the following

morning Dino sets out on foot towards Switzerland; he
ascends along a valley (the Val Divedro) bristling with 'towers of steel', that is, the steel pylons carrying the electric
power cables from the Alpine generators down towards the
Po valley. At Iselle he sees the entrance to the Simplon
tunnel, the longest in the world, and thinks with reverence
of that silent steadfast Italy which 'has brought itself to
drive through rock.' Trooping along with other emigrants
(many of them carrying their spades on their shoulders as
their only passport), he crosses the Swiss border and ascends
further, with his slow, swinging highlander's gait, up to
the Simplon's two-thousand-metre altitude; then descends
towards Brig. In Berne over the next few months he partly
works as a porter and a navvy ('here they detest as a
monstrosity any Italian who is anything more than a helot')
and partly completes the re-writing of his book, modifying
its structure and adding completely new texts to those
rescued from the jottings for his first manuscript. The idea
of the title *Orphic Songs* comes to him from a book by
Schuré, *L'évolution divine du Sphinx au Christ*. In May he
lands in gaol, certainly for some trifling matter which is
not recorded either by the Italian consulate or by the Can-
tonal police. 'I'd quarrelled with a Swiss,' Dino will later
tell Pariani. 'Bruises. I wasn't convicted. I had a relative
who vouched for me.' The relative is his Uncle Francesco
Campana, who has in the meantime been transferred from
Florence to Pisa and promoted to Chief Procurator of the
High Court there. The cause of the quarrel is unknown and
may be quite banal – a shove or an insult. It's anybody's
guess. Later, back in the madhouse, Dino will rule out any
connection between this incident in 1914 and the image in
one of his prose pieces of 'a lady' in Berne who falls in love
with the 'handsome foreigner'. ('It's all fantasy.' 'If anything
that figure belongs in Geneva.') Only two things are certain.
The first is that after his arrest Dino feels 'desperate and
lost in the world' and sends his friend Bandini the manuscript of the *Canti Orfici* so as to make sure that it does not

go missing again. ('It testifies to something in my favour, perhaps it testifies to my not having deserved my fate.') The second is that, a few days after the arrival of the parcel at the Bandinis', Dino reappears in Marradi: without a cent in his pocket but more determined than ever to publish the *Canti Orfici* in despite of all the publishers and Florentine littérateurs... 'I need to get into print: to prove to myself that I exist, to go on writing I need to get into print.' 'I'm not ambitious, but I think that after having been kicked around the world, after having let life tear me to pieces, my words which nevertheless rise upwards have the right to be listened to.'

To print the *Canti Orfici*, the typographer Bruno Ravagli (not to be confused with Dino's biographer Federico Ravagli or with the scholar Francesco Ravagli) asks for six hundred and fifty lire, two hundred to be paid in advance to cover costs. The *cavalier* Bandini opens a subscription list among the members of the Società Operaia: forty copies of the book are bespoke by the workers of Marradi and their subscription price paid to 'Gigino'. ('None of your townsfolk,' the poet says to him, 'would trust me with a cent. You see to it.') For his own part, Dino is convinced that he can gather fifty or sixty subscriptions from among the students in Bologna and the artists in Florence. In fact, he only manages to collect four, after scouring both cities from end to end and enduring all sorts of mortifications, especially in Florence: where word has gone round that he's after money and everybody dashes away from him, turns the corner, pretends to be not at home, and anyone who simply can't dodge him pre-empts his pleas by telling him tear-jerking tales of his own debts and straitened circumstances. Hurt, disappointed, Dino unburdens himself to Bandini ('What with rejections by publishers and imagined betrayals by friends – and their indifference at least was real enough – he raved and ranted.') In the end, he gives in, he recognizes that two hundred lire is too large a sum to collect from the sales of a book which has not yet been printed: but, without the two hundred lire, the book never will be printed... 'Life is a vicious circle.' 'Gigino', witnessing his distress, has a word with his father: couldn't Dino be helped out? The *cavalier* Bandini goes to see the typographer Ravagli, secretly gives him some money (a hundred?) out of his own pocket; and so, finally, on 7 June 1914, with Fabroni Camillo and Bandini Luigi as witnesses, a contract is drawn up under which Signor Bruno Ravagli will print Signor Dino Campana's book *Canti Orfici* in a thousand copies 'within the month of July next' and will put it on sale 'at the price of lire two fifty per volume'. Twenty copies – so runs the contract – will belong to the author; the rest of the print-run will be held at the printer's until Ravagli has been reimbursed 'from sales' the monies due to him.

The end of June sees the correction of proofs. In July the book goes to press, and it is at this point that the 'Campana legend' for once is close to the truth in describing to us poor Ravagli grappling with Dino's revisions, and being forced to reprint pages which have been already printed and folded ready for the binder. (In the end, the book is made up of three different kinds of paper.) And when all is done, Dino still makes him remove the index and replace it with an English phrase (*They were all torn and cover'd with the boy's blood*) of uncertain meaning: what is meant by 'the boy's blood'? Who is the boy in question? – And in the evenings he rows with the worthies of the *Comune* and of the Circolo and then, the following morning, dashes over to the printer's to add phrases in German to the cover, a dedication 'to Wilhelm II'...

In order to understand 'the tragedy of the last of the Germans in Italy' (*Die Tragödie des letzten Germanen in Italien*) in the subtitle of the *Canti Orfici*, and the dedication to the Emperor Wilhelm II, attention must be paid to certain events taking place in Europe while Ravagli is printing Campana's book, and to the repercussions which they have in Marradi: which, since 1910, has had a mayor with D'Annunzian leanings (in June 1912 the Marradi administration was in the news for voting a sum of money to 'Italy's air-fleet'); and where the gentry are all united in their ardent nationalism, which will soon lead them to support the campaign for Italy's intervention in the European war against her allies of over thirty years' standing, Germany and Austria-Hungary. The events in question are: the assassination in Sarajevo on 28 June 1914 of Archduke Franz Ferdinand, heir to the Austrian throne; the anti-Austrian and anti-German campaign mounted in Italy; the mounting international tension leading, at the end of July, to the first declaration of war (that by Austria on Serbia), with others following. (Germany's on Russia; Germany's on France; Britain's on Germany, etc.) At the Circolo Marradese and in the cafés on Piazza Scalelle, all the talk is of nothing else. 'Germanophobes, Francophiles, Freemasons and Jesuits, all of them always said the same things: and the Kaiser's a murderer, and little children have their hands cut off, and our Latin sister, and it's a war against militarism.' One evening, jeered at by his fellow-Marradians, Dino starts to inveigh against 'the Marradi rabble', or rather, 'the Italian rabble', who – he says – 'must be crushed by whatever means.' Standing in the middle of the piazza he yells at them: 'I spit on you,' and he actually does spit, 'on your God, on your women, on your children, on your laws.' 'I want to renounce my Italian citizenship. I want to enlist for the Kaiser.'

So it is that, after this scene, is born the idea of the dedication 'to William II Emperor of the Germans': which the Socialist Ravagli agrees to print because he really finds it rather funny . . . But the ultimate significance of the subtitle and of the English epigraph is to be found in the testamentary letter of March 1916 to Emilio Cecchi, already quoted: 'If you take any further interest in me, alive or dead,' writes the poet, 'I beg you not to forget the final words *They were all torn and cover'd with the boy's blood* which are the only important words in the book.' 'Now I said *die Tragödie des letzten Germanen in Italien,* showing that in the book I'd preserved the moral purity of the German (ideal, not real), taken as representative of the superior moral type (Dante Leopardi Segantini).'*

---

* Giovanni Segantini (1858-1899), a 'divisionist' (almost equivalent to 'impressionist') painter from the Trentino. He painted mostly landscapes, especially Alpine. – Trs.

As the carnage begins in the Balkans and along the lower Rhine, Dino despatches copies of his book to the literary grandees: to Benedetto Croce, to Giovanni Verga, to Ferdinando Martini, to Ugo Ojetti, to Giuseppe Prezzolini... Verga sends 'a laconic card' in reply; the others, nothing, and their silence, for the author, is cause for everlasting anathema. Those who receive a complimentary copy of the *Canti* include Giovanni Papini and Ardengo Soffici. The latter, who knows why, later says he bought the book 'from a bookseller in Via dei Martelli'. Soffici has kept Dino's manuscript in his cupboard for nine months, yet for him reading the *Canti* comes as a completely new experience. As he says in his *Ricordi*: 'I read the book from cover to cover, getting from it an impression of broad sunlight which saturated me with its strong sweetness, comparable to that of a ripe fruit, fragrant, exquisite. Still under the impress of such poetic felicity, without further ado, I wrote Campana a fine letter expressing my feelings and my gratitude and sent it to him in Marradi.'

Early in September 1914 Dino reappears in Florence, better dressed than heretofore and determined to live off the proceeds of selling his book just as any other artist lives by selling his work: music, paintings, plays... In order to boost trade he acts his self-appointed role of 'boy' and 'Germanic poet'. He makes sudden sallies into the third saloon of the Giubbe Rosse café, where the teenage literary mob gloomily discusses the German military successes; 'red-faced, his blue eyes sparkling', he celebrates 'the beauty and the joy of the first Uhlan to ride into a French town' (Soffici). Then leaves. On the square he offers his 'wares' to the people seated at the tables: he negotiates over the price, displays the contents. He keeps his reputation as a 'madman' green: but this period of calculated eccentricity is perhaps the most sober-sided in Dino's life, the only time when he enjoys some respect and also some consideration. Papini and Soffici try to domesticate him: they publish some of his pieces in *Lacerba*, with a not wholly unequivocal editorial note ('These three chunks of poetic ore are taken from a book of *Orphic Songs* which is just out and which we will be discussing'); they introduce him to Marinetti – to whom Dino sells a copy of *Canti Orfici* minus three or four pages – and to other passing celebrities, no longer presenting him as 'unbalanced'. Papini seems particularly ingratiating. He gives him Bertrand Russell's *The Problems of Philosophy* to translate for publication by Carabba and pays him an advance; he invites him to dinner one evening: and thus discovers a quite unheard-of side to Dino's character. The poet is too 'primitive' or perhaps too shy to sit down to dinner in somebody else's house. 'He turned up extremely late, when the table had already been cleared, and wouldn't accept a thing... He said he'd recollected the invitation when it was too late and that he'd only come to give his thanks' (Papini). 'He had agreed, very reluctantly, to stay to dinner with us, together with Giannotto Bastianelli; but he sat himself at the table askew, in the posture and role of a spectator rather than a fellow-diner, since, being of rustic disposition, he couldn't bring himself to eat and drink in someone else's house' (Leonetta Cecchi Pieraccini).

In the winter of 1914 a new episode enters the 'Campana legend': that of the poet who suddenly stops being 'Germanic' and erases the dedications and subtitles from the copies of his book, 'shutting himself away in a backroom of the bookseller Gonnelli's'. 'For days and days,' says Soffici, 'armed with pen-knife and rubber, he rubbed, cut, pasted: the paper would tear just when he was getting it right, the strips gummed over the ill-fated characters spoiled the cover; but there you are: Campana had no peace until everything was obliterated.'

Apart from the heightened tone, the story is true, and the reason behind it, which Soffici does not mention though he was certainly aware of it, is a visit by the police to Gonnelli's bookshop. One morning in December two uniformed policemen enter the shop in Via Cavour and talk to the bookseller and writer Ugo Tommei, ask to see a copy of the volume entitled *Canti Orfici* which is in the showcase, leaf through it and copy out some phrases: the German subtitle, the dedication to William II Emperor of the Germans, the English epigraph on the last page. From Tommei the police also collect information regarding the author: where he's from, where he lives, what his livelihood is, who his friends are... Tommei tells them what he knows and takes the matter fairly lightly; in fact he is amazed by Dino's reaction on hearing of the matter: he appears literally distraught. Tommei bursts out laughing: 'Now calm down. What on earth do you expect to happen. You haven't murdered anyone.' Dino Campana accuses him in fury of having been the one who reported him to the police; of having been – along with Papini, Prezzolini and the others of the *Voce* group – the instigator and author of all the police persecution that he's had to undergo. He flies into a rage in the street (Soffici relates): he storms at two of the town watch, seizes a *Voce* man by the throat... Early the next day he shuts himself in Gonnelli's back room and deals with the copies of the *Canti* which are held in the bookshop: he removes the page with the dedication and over the line about the tragedy of the last of the Germans he sticks a strip of adhesive paper. Then he leaves. He goes to Pisa and sees his uncle Francesco, who advises him to remove the first page from all the copies of the book, because, he says, 'no one can foretell what's going to happen in the next few months.' 'What if Italy, as now seems likely, were to enter the war against Germany?' At the beginning of 1915 he sails to Sardinia: he has a few lire in his pocket and he wants to sell his book to his friends there. But his friends are not to be found, Sardinia is an 'arid and discouraging' land and the lire melt away fast. At the end of January he is in Turin. He sells some copies of the *Canti Orfici* to the editorial staff of the *Gazzetta del Popolo*, where Francini is working, and for over a month is a salesboy for the same newspaper, yelling out the headlines ('Winter offensive in Champagne!' 'Demonstrations in Milan in favour of Italian intervention!') under the arcades of Via Po, of Piazza Castello, of Via Roma. He's in good spirits and writes to tell Papini that he means to complete the translation of Russell which he began in Florence; he sends greetings to 'my friends of *La Voce*, Gonnelli and Tommei. I bear no grudges against anyone, I have fond memories of all.' In mid-March he goes to Switzerland with a letter of introduction from the Marradi Società Operaia to the Geneva Committee of Italian Societies. But Switzerland is full of draft dodgers of all nations and work opportunities are few and far between. Between one job and another Dino becomes familiar with the Offices for the assistance of Italians abroad: 'The Dante Alighieri Society sends me to the Opera Bonomelli soup-kitchen.' He sells a copy of the *Canti Orfici* to a shifty-looking German who a few days later returns with another German: 'You are ze last of ze Ghermans in Italien?' Dino gives him a baffled look, and the other explains that His Imperial Highness Wilhelm II, the Kaiser, is not insensitive to the tragedy of the last of the Germans in Italy, and indeed would like to help them, in return for some small services... Out comes a fat wallet: 'I give money *im foraus*. How you say Italian? Advance.' Dino gets rid of him: 'Clear off!' – He also works as a labourer and on 6 May receives a testimonial: *'Nous avons occupé Dino Campana et avons été très satisfaits de son travail.'* On 12 May, in Geneva, he has an adventure with 'a Segantinian Switzerwoman' whom he met 'in a café with girls, barrel-organs, wall-mirrors, ripe lasses, glass beads, chocolate and that so very sweet bad taste which is characteristic of Switzerland'. This is the first time that spending two hours with a woman costs him only 'ten minutes chitchat and one lira in room-rent' and so he declares himself 'moved by the simplicity of life and love'. On 15 May, in the evening, in the station buffet at Domodossola, he dashes off the first draft of the 'Canto proletario italo-francese', containing images from the previous year – the Val Divedro landscape, the Simplon tunnel, the labourers filing along with their spades over their shoulders – and more recent overtones of war, to a rhythm which occasionally takes on the cadence of a military march: 'Dear Italy what do you care / You've brought yourself to drive through rock / This time take courage here, / for the door will open to you.'

Dino goes back to Marradi because he can't make a living in Switzerland and because he expects Italy's entry into the war, which everybody now considers imminent, will work the miracle of restoring him to his full rights as a citizen and to 'normality'. He wants to enlist, to go to the front. On 24 May 1915, after Italy has declared war on the Austro-Hungarian Empire, Dino presents himself with his wicker basket at district military headquarters, passes his medical examination, wears the uniform... When it is discovered that he is a certified lunatic, he is rudely thrown out; but in the meantime the news that 'the madman' has volunteered gets around Marradi, to the discomfiture of those heroes of the day before yesterday who, now that they should be enlisting, have remembered their family responsibilities, their infirmities. Naturally their embarrassment evaporates the moment Dino reappears in town; in fact there are such goings-on – including turds on the doorstep and farting serenades – that Fanny on her own initiative breaks her husband's prohibition and gives her son twenty-five lire as long as he gets out of the way: 'Go and stay with your uncle and aunt at Premilcuore.' – In July, Dino is unwell: he has nocturnal migraines and intermittent delirium. He wants to escape from the 'clerical beasts' in his country, move to France: why isn't he allowed a passport? He believes himself to be the victim of a plot hatched by Buci-vini Capecchi, by deputy mayor Ceroni, by the members of the Circolo Marradese, and he writes to Papini, to Soffici, to Prezzolini: can they put in a word for him, help him obtain a passport for France? As they don't reply, he assumes that they are also in the plot. (Just like Gonnelli, Tommei and the *La Voce* writers: haven't they already reported him to the police for the dedication to the *Canti Orfici*? Haven't they 'kidnapped' his manuscript so as to prevent its publication?) He has bouts of fever and persistent pains in the liver, in the spleen, in the kidneys: the doctor thinks he may have Bright's disease. By the end of August he is better and he sets out for Turin, he wants to join his friends of *La Gazzetta del Popolo* who are on holiday at Rubiana in the Val di Susa: but he has reckoned without the war-time conditions, the checkpoints at railway stations, the maniacal searches for deserters, for spies . . . The *carabinieri* stop him at Turin station, and he, to prove his identity, shows them a copy of the *Canti*; he shows them two articles, one by someone called Binazzi in *Il Mattino* and the other by someone else called De Robertis in *La Voce*. (Both Binazzi and De Robertis being, of course, well-known literary critics, but not to the *carabinieri*.) 'They're writing about me. I'm the one.' He's confined in a cell, then sent back to Marradi, where superintendent Anonymous sends for Torquato Campana to remind him of the responsibility which he's taken on as legal guardian of a mental patient. 'These are difficult times,' he says. 'The country is teeming with deserters and anyone unable to prove his identity should stay put: understood?' But Dino escapes to Florence, spends a fortnight there, selling a few copies of *Canti Orfici* and getting meals at the Daily Bread Society. Until one morning he discovers himself in the same state as Regolo in Genoa, 'his right side paralysed, the cast in his eye staring at this phenomenon'. His right arm is completely limp and he finds it hard to raise his right foot, and the leg is heavy, too. Hobbling down one street after another, leaning against lamp-posts and walls to rest, Dino gets to the hospital; but he can't pay for admission, and the duty doctor, without even examining him, tells him that his affliction isn't really so serious as to prevent him returning home. Where does he live? 'Marradi.' There you are, proclaims the doctor: they even have a hospital there. What more do you want from life? 'Go back to Marradi and get some treatment. Soon your class will be called up, too, and you too will have to go off to the front.'

The tragedy of the 'last of the Germans' is now nearing its epilogue. Between the end of October and the first half of December, Dino Campana spends about six weeks in the Marradi hospital, officially being treated for Bright's disease. Nothing is known about the therapy: but his repeated and violent fevers, his delirious ravings against the 'murderers' among his fellow townsmen who come and 'whistle beneath the windows' or against the doctors who want to 'fool' him ('I haven't got Bright's disease,' howls Dino, 'I have a cerebral congestion!') might suggest the malarial therapy which is the commonest treatment for venereal diseases at the beginning of the century. In a word, it cannot be ruled out that the Marradi medical staff in fact recognize and treat the illness of 'the son of the director of schools' as syphilis. (For a year, that is since he has had to resign his post after reaching the age limit, schoolmaster Giovanni Campana has been director of education 'in charge' of schools at Lastra a Signa, a few kilometres from Florence.) But this diagnosis, if made, is kept hidden and is only revealed to the elderly parent in great secrecy and with all sorts of palliatives, so that he needn't be put to unnecessary shame. ('What can one do about it... Young men...' 'They want everything instantly and then we have to look after them.' 'Did you but know the number of cases we get...')

In mid-December Dino leaves hospital, underweight and with a slight limp. His right eye has acquired a cast, as appears from the portrait by Costetti and from the photograph taken at Castel Pulci in 1928. His hair has grown thinner. His mind is clear, but intermittently, with delirious spells and obsessions: the 'clerical beasts' of Marradi, the passport denied him, the 'kidnapped' manuscript, the Florentine writers 'torn and cover'd with the boy's blood'... He wants to cure himself in his own way ('Now I'll recover on my own') so as to be fit enough, when the thaw comes, to return to Switzerland on foot. ('At the thaw I'll be able to vault across the Swiss Alps if necessary.') He buys a can full of leeches and applies them to his temples to alleviate his 'cerebral congestion' during the night, when his headaches are excruciating: 'Now at last after two months in hospital I've had to apply leeches myself, last remnant of the barbarians in Italy.'

Papini's behaviour in asking to see his manuscript purely for form's sake and then never reading it or returning it keeps returning to the forefront of Dino's thoughts as the memory of an unbearable wrong and as being emblematic of the literary pursuit as mere 'Machiavellianism', 'a cerebral technique', 'toads and serpents and snake-charmer', 'a corpse-factory', 'bourgeois phrase-mongering'. Of the literary pursuit as 'the negation of God, that is, the negation of art'. On 5 January 1916 Dino writes to Ardengo Soffici (who is at the front) from Marradi requesting the return of his manuscript: 'I am writing to you so that you will send me my famous manuscript which I will never but never forgive you for having kidnapped from me. Just imagine for a moment that you're a Frenchman, and you'll realize the enormity of what you've done.' On 23 January 1916, having had no reply, he writes to Papini: 'If within a week I haven't received the manuscript and the other papers I handed to you three years ago I shall come to Florence with a good knife and I will see justice done wherever I find you.' (Papini reads this, aghast. 'Then it's true, he *is* mad!') He replies, calling Dino a madman and threatening to pass the letter on to the police if he causes any further nuisance. In February Dino is in Bologna, where he sees Binazzi, Ravegnani and others. His obsession over the manuscript pursues him wherever he goes. From Marradi in March he writes the testamentary letter to Cecchi telling the story of his life. He wants to challenge Soffici to a duel. Cecchi replies gently: 'I've known you to suffer over certain things that frankly are not worth the bother.' But Dino won't listen to reason. He dashes over to Florence, roves the strangely silent squares and streets, with no tourists or young people to be seen. Wall-posters urge the citizen not to talk to strangers and to report any suspicious individuals. They exalt the endeavour of the Fatherland. At the Giubbe Rosse Dino finds only Raffaello Franchi, a seventeen-year-old poet who has already been published by Gonnelli. Dino sells him a copy of the *Canti Orfici* and walks along with him for a few hundred metres. He holds forth animatedly against Papini and Soffici, whom he accuses of being the corrupters of the nation's art and mores. He promises he will take justice into his own hands; even if, he says, the evil weed has roots that sink as far back as the Renaissance and Machiavelli and has spread throughout European culture, especially in France. His indictment reaches its conclusion 'beyond Ponte Vecchio, where, beneath a nude statue by an unknown Tuscan sculptor, an ancient sarcophagus equipped with great fake masks fulfils its function as a tank'. That is where, as Franchi remembers it, 'Campana burst into a bitter invective against Machiavelli and Rimbaud, seducers of the young, destroyers of every healthy tradition.' 'We stopped at the foot of the disguised sarcophagus. Campana's predictions were as sinister as the news of a massacre, and they were at the same time obscure in the attempt to spell things out logically, obscure and tightly packed... Round about, the peaceable shops remained unaffected. The grocer, the chemist, the greengrocer busied themselves, one over a crate of fine fruit, the others at their counters, in perspective, beyond the enamelled lettering on their glass doors. Invincible monotony, sustained by the harmonious outlines of the palaces, presented a solid block in space and time so that one couldn't even understand from whence, nor by what treachery, history could roll along. Only the two of us, the tone of our discourse clashing with the approaching hour for lunch, seemed to impinge on the circumambient reality in an original abstractedness from the here and now. Our parting was abrupt, inconsequential, heavy with remorse.'

One morning in April Dino bursts into the *La Voce* book-shop: he's looking for Papini, who isn't there. He finds the 'filthy lout' De Robertis, whom he accuses of being 'in league with criminals'. He then rushes over to Via Colletta, where his 'arch-enemy' has recently bought himself an apartment; he shoves past the housemaid who opens the door and halfway down the corridor runs into Papini's eldest daughter, Viola. 'Where's your father's study?' The child points to a door, which he opens. He enters. He looks at the shelves stacked with books, the manuscripts and newspapers neatly arranged on the desk and naturally he ought to charge forward and turn the whole place upside down, but his resolution has failed by now, his excitement has died down. He turns, says: 'I'll be back.' And disappears from sight down the stairs.

He goes to stay with his father at Lastra a Signa, where he remains for over a month without a cent. ('I'm under arrest at Signa for lack of funds.') He writes to friends and acquaintances asking them to help him find 'some small employment', even 'mechanical' employment, so as to earn a little; a job as a translator, or as a level-crossing keeper. ('I'd like to mind the Genoa-Voghera line.') At night he yells out, he raves. The malarial therapy notwithstanding, he is far from being cured: his right leg is 'much heavier than the other', the headaches return each night, his obsessions plague him. Seeing he is badly ill, schoolmaster Giovanni Campana gives him a small sum of money so as to go to the seaside to 'convalesce', at the house of the Marradi painter Bianca Fabroni Minucci (known in art as 'Donnabianca') at Antignano, near Leghorn. For appearance's sake, and to avoid gossip, it is agreed that Dino should not sleep in the Minuccis' villa, so he rents a room in Leghorn, goes to Antignano in the mornings and returns to town in the evenings: he reads, writes, converses with the lady of the house or with her extremely beautiful guest Lusena, who is in the Red Cross, has lost her fiancé in the fighting and is now waiting to go to the front. He strolls, alone, along the seashore. He feels that poetry is eluding him, that it won't return: 'O poetry, you will not return / Elegance, elegance / Drawn bow of beauty. / The flesh is tired, the brain is clouding, tiring / Palm-trees grey and odourless reach up / Facing the waste of the sea / The cubes of the tall buildings tower up.' He talks of it half in shock and half in grief: 'Write I cannot, my nerves can no longer take it.' 'I don't want to go on being a poet. Even the waters and even the silence no longer have anything to say to me, and infinite is my desolation.'

He muses on the present, on the future. He plans to make a living, when the war is over, by putting his knowledge of languages to use 'after having desisted from literature in all its forms'. He'd like to realize some cash by selling off the entire stock of the *Canti Orfici* as a job lot to a book distributor or even by offering it 'to His Majesty'. Literary success concerns him not at all. When the critic Emilio Cecchi announces to him that he's written an article about him for the newspaper *La Tribuna*, Dino replies ingenuously: 'I would request you to direct me to some dealer who would relieve me of the last few hundred copies of the Canti, and that would be possible after the publication of your article, would it not?'

On Wednesday 31 May 1916 in Piazza Cavalleggeri in Leghorn Dino approaches two women to ask them (according to the report in the daily *Il Telegrafo*) the way to the Orlando shipyards and the Naval Academy. Terrified, the women answer that they know nothing, and rush to inform an excise officer, one Giuliano Barluzzi: there's a young man, they say, with a foreign accent and of German appearance who's wandering around gathering information about shipyards and military establishments. 'Where is he?' asks Barluzzi. Following the directions given, he approaches the suspect, arrests him without meeting any resistance, and 'conveys' him to police headquarters. Here, after several hours' delay (during which time the police search his room), Dino is sat in front of a desk with an electric light shining in his eyes, and questioned 'lengthily' by Superintendent Schiavetti and by Inspector Frenguelli. He is taxed, as usual, with not having documents; with not being in uniform; of having some copies, in his suitcase, of a book, apparently of poetry, with writing in German and other writing in Italian hailing 'William II Emperor of the Germans'... Given the state of war and restrictions on liberty that apply to everybody, Dino's situation (suspected of desertion, of propaganda for the enemy and, why not? of espionage) is such that if his uncle were not Procurator Royal in Pisa he would land straight in gaol and would stay there goodness knows how long before he could clarify his position; instead of which, he is released the same day. ('His Excellency'

Francesco Campana, contacted by telephone, confirms his nephew's particulars and adds some others which secure his immediate release. He says he's been in an asylum, that indeed, in law, he's still there. 'That is why,' he explains, 'he wasn't taken by the army.' He says he's had Bright's disease and is now convalescing by the sea.) But only three weeks later Superintendent Schiavetti sees him pop up again, hauled in by two of the town watch who declare that they have arrested him because, while under the influence of alcohol, he described himself as a 'Germanic poet' and said more besides: for instance, that he'd had dealings in Geneva, in the spring of 1915, with an emissary of the Kaiser, who purportedly made him some 'interesting proposals'. Alone with Dino, the superintendent gives him a brief lecture which, as to content and style, can be summarized as follows: 'I've had enough of you. If you're mad, that's your affair, but you've got to clear out of Leghorn by tomorrow, is that clear? If I see you here again...'

During the night from Tuesday 20th to Wednesday 21st May, Dino is in delirium, imagines that an entire town – Leghorn – is in the plot against him. He writes a letter to *Il Telegrafo* accusing the people of Leghorn of being all 'criminals and in league with criminals', 'pimps and spies'. He signs it 'Dino Campana, Germanic poet'; packs his bag and catches the train, but does not forget to post the letter before leaving for Florence. On the following day, Thursday, the second page of *Il Telegrafo* carries an article, half humorous, half paternalistic, entitled 'Signor Dino Campana, Germanic poet'. The article, signed by Athos Gastone Banti, founder and first editor-in-chief of the Leghorn newspaper, defines the poet as 'a creature ugly and strange, red-haired and shady-looking' who 'makes idiotic speeches in public: stupid speeches: cretinous speechs: speeches of... an Italo-Germanic poet'. In Lastra a Signa, where he has gone back to stay with his father, the 'creature' reads this and decides that he will cleanse the insult with blood, according to the rules of chivalry. He writes his challenge

('You are a grotesque negro half-caste and an out-and-out idiot, and therefore in calling myself Germanic I was giving you a kick in the arse') and before mailing it he has it countersigned by a witness: one 'Mario Moschi, sculptor'. During the night between Friday and Saturday Dino's obsessions reach a paroxysm. Banti, whom he does not know, variously appears to him in the semblance of the 'screw' Papini, of the 'jackal' Bucivini Capecchi, of the 'snake' Carrà who has publicly insulted him, and all of a sudden, in his delirium, this last identification becomes a certainty. But of course! Banti, the hoodlum, is Carrà, who is acting on behalf of the 'bags of pus coated with Futurism', that is, Papini, Soffici, Marinetti... Howling on his rumpled bed, flailing among the bedsheets, Dino keeps repeating, 'It's the eve.' He'd like to write to Carrà: to tell him that he, 'poet of the present and of the future', knows everything and has understood everything. However, he doesn't know Carrà's address and he decides that he will write to Papini. ('After all, one bag of pus is as good as another.') He gets up, sits down at the desk. In the absence of notepaper, he uses the back of an envelope: 'Carrà will remember me (he recommended I should come to Florence dressed in goatskin). So, then, until I have the pleasure of running you through. Is this the eve?'

His head feels so heavy that at times Dino props himself up so as not to pitch forwards. He writes: 'I am indifferent, I who live at the foot of innumerable Calvaries. Everybody has spat at me since I was fourteen, I hope that someone at last will run me through. But you should know that you won't be running through a bag of pus but the supreme alchemist who has transformed suffering into blood. Hurrah! I want to run through or be run through in loathing of those bags of pus coated with Futurism.'

On Saturday 24 June 1916, shortly after eight o'clock in the morning, Dino is still asleep and a messenger awakens him, makes him sign the receipt for a telegram from Livorno sent by a certain Giacomo Merli, a retired general, and a certain Marco Tonci dell'Acciaia, a Count, the seconds nominated by the *cavalier* Athos Gastone Banti for his duel with Campana. They formally request the challenger to name his own representatives. Dino washes, gets dressed, still fatigued from his nightmares, goes to the post office, telegraphs to General Merli: I name as my representatives Signor M. Moschi, sculptor, and Signor A. Takeda, painter. That afternoon in Florence he talks to the Japanese Takeda, who is descended from a family of samurai and is an expert in martial arts, and who readily agrees to be his second. Night has fallen by the time he arrives back in Signa, and he finds on the doormat a card from Moschi: 'Telegram received from Leghorn. I urgently wish to see you.' Dino is puzzled: what could he be after? After a few hours' sleep interspersed with his usual nightmares, he dashes over to Moschi's studio (it is now Sunday morning) and Moschi shows him the telegram from the implacable General Merli and Count Tonci dell'Acciaia who under article 130 of the code of honour summon the opposing seconds to meet them at 'fourteen hundred hours tomorrow' at the Circolo Filologico in Leghorn. 'Two o'clock this afternoon,' explains Moschi to poor Dino, who has turned to stone. 'What have you replied?' asks Dino. Moschi spreads out his arms: 'Nothing. I haven't answered at all.' He explains: 'A joke is a joke, but these guys give me the creeps, and besides, I've never seen a duel in my life, I have no wish to go to Leghorn, in a word, I can't undertake to be your second. Find yourself someone more suitable.'

Even 'to run through or be run through' is an enterprise not without its difficulties. What's to be done? Dino sends Takeda an envelope containing the telegram and himself goes to Florence in search of another second to replace Moschi; but doesn't find one. The experts on honour are all away at the front; those left behind 'for reasons of health' (painters and writers who, on average, will live to be a hundred) are useless for this kind of business. After trying for two days Dino reluctantly withdraws from his war against the 'bags of pus'. His mind has now almost fully cleared, the pressure on his head at night is less painful, and his deliriums have gone. Early in July, with sixty lire from his father in his pocket, he goes to Barco near Rifredo in the mountains of the Mugello in Tuscany. Here, in 'the real landscape of solitaries', he hopes at last to restore himself and to reorganize his life around something other than poetry.

Dino seriously intends to abandon his art, to find a job. He writes to everyone he knows: can they get him 'some small job', 'a livelihood of two lire per day'? (His father is already giving him two lire per day until he has set himself up again.) Nobody takes him seriously. His only two sources of income are the sale of the *Canti Orfici*, personally or through the mail, and his work for *Riviera Ligure*, a literary journal with a difference: born as a publicity handout for the olive-oil factory owned by the brothers Mario and Angiolo Silvio Novaro, it is distributed with crates of oil and is not to be found at newsagents'. *Riviera Ligure* sent Dino a royalty of one hundred lire in January and would send him more money if he had material to publish: but he hasn't. (In May, urgently in need of cash, he almost stooped to plagiarism by receiving payment for a poem by the Florentine poetess Luisa Giaconi, who had died in 1908, as if it were his own.) All he can offer is himself, and in fact he does offer himself to the Novaros: do they need a translator, a clerk, a half-time employee for the oil factory or the journal? Mario answers that they don't, and so his work for *Riviera Ligure* also comes to an end.

From Barco, where he's staying 'in a common tavern', Dino descends one day in mid-July to Scarperia to pay a visit to a certain Anna who has bought a copy of the *Canti Orfici* off him at the Giubbe Rosse in Florence and then written him a letter cluttered with exclamation marks, vocatives and hyperboles. This Anna Unsurnamed (perhaps she has a Slav surname) is the 'incredible Russian woman from Africa' about whom Dino tells tall stories to Emilio Cecchi and Sibilla Aleramo but about whom, out of shamefacedness, he gives no information. All we know about her is that she agrees to pay the rent for the poet's lodgings in Casetta di Tiara, a village right on top of the Apennine ridge between the Futa and Raticosa passes, without asking in exchange for anything more than the privilege of seeing him from time to time. We may therefore suppose that she is neither young nor beautiful nor particularly talented in literature or art. Dino's meetings with Anna take place in the second half of July and are motivated on Dino's part first and foremost by his need to settle the Casetta 'deal': which will enable him to survive away from Marradi on his father's two lire a day. Meanwhile, other matters are coming to a head. On 3 August, a Thursday, at 7.30 in the morning, Dino is sitting on a low wall just outside the village and watching, in the direction of Scarperia, the 'mail' coach from Florence approaching in a cloud of dust to halt a few metres away from him. From it alights a single passenger – a lady dressed in white, wearing the broadest-brimmed of hats, with a 'regal' bearing. Unusually obliging, the driver spares no effort in unloading her luggage – her travelling bag, her handbag, her parasol – but she doesn't even notice, walks up to Dino, who has got to his feet, is smiling at her. She asks, 'Are you Dino Campana?' She holds out her hand, and says: 'Here I am. I'm Sibilla.'

Dino's meeting with Sibilla at Barco is preceded by an exchange of letters which serve above all to overcome his initial distrust, his very real misogyny (exacerbated at this very time by the business with 'the Russian woman'). Dino wants an affair without problems or aftermaths – an affair like the one with the 'Segantinian Switzerwoman' which so 'touched' him a year ago – but Aleramo's man-eating reputation alarms him and he writes to Cecchi for advice, reassurance, protection... Sibilla is concerned about quite different things. She's decided on the affair at the very moment when she finished reading *Canti Orfici* ('Your book I close / My hair I loose'), and her opening gambit letters are the preliminaries to an encounter which she will accept on any terms and in any place, though she would prefer Dino to make the first move... ('If you had come here, I might have made a better first impression on you, without a hat and all the other impedimenta of a journey.')

Rina Faccio, Sibilla to the world of art, is exactly forty in August 1916, having been born in Alessandria, in Piedmont, in August 1876. She is, like Dino, a Leo. She recounts, in her novel *Una donna* (A Woman), her infancy, her childhood, her violation at the age of fifteen, 'made good' by an absurd marriage, the birth of her only child and, soon after, separation... 'Something inside me has remained eternally dissatisfied,' says Faccio-Aleramo, 'the yearning for a love-child, a creature to be at one and the same time a masterpiece produced by my body, my heart, my spirit. And I have loved, or thought I loved, so many men. And that's how my poetry was generated.' At the time of her meeting with Dino the roster of Sibilla's former lovers already includes almost the whole of living Italian literature, a good part of the figurative arts, some representatives of the theatrical world and an unspecified number of aviators, horsemen, revolutionaries and bankers with whom her 'eternally dis-satisfied' spirit has had 'easy' yet 'vertiginously intense' rela-tions. ('We were one single moan.') Her face is that of Italy holding an ear of corn as seen on the twenty-cent coins, created by the sculptor Leonardo Bistolfi. (One of the 'many', datable to 1908 or 1909.) Her more intimate features are displayed by Michele Cascella (another one) in a series of nudes exhibited in Rome and Milan and subsequently also reproduced in a book of poems which De Robertis in *La Voce* curtly dismissed as 'chic lyrics'...

Sibilla is already in love, she's already come up here with her eyes full of 'a vision of strength and grandeur, outside time'. Dino has no mind for love, but only for an affair with a woman older than himself but still handsome and ready: and he goes straight to the point. (Sibilla: 'Always before my eyes is that road in the sun on that first morning, the springs at which you slaked my thirst, the earth mingling with our kisses, that deep embrace of light.') He lets her do the talking, about herself, about her life – you've already written everything down in your books, why are you saying it all? – and in a word behaves like someone with experience, a man of the world, sees to the material practicalities: her room in the inn, lunch, dinner, their after-dinner walk. (Sibilla: 'Our bodies on the hard clods, the wheatears brushing against our brows, while the stars deepen the skydark.') He utters shrewd words. (Sibilla: 'You said: you don't say: *always, never*, like other women.')

Dino doesn't think he has any real interest in Sibilla, much less that he could fall in love with her. And besides, what does it mean to 'fall in love'? (At thirty-one, he has never been 'in love'.) Stuff out of women's novels...He's satisfied, yes. He's got what he wanted: an affair up among his mountains with a woman he likes, who gives herself without any fuss...His defences begin to break down at the moment when he realizes that the 'affair' doesn't end in three days. On Sunday 6 August, an hour before Sibilla catches the coach back, Dino asks her to return, then stammers, flushes, comes out with words he'd never have thought he could bring himself to utter. (Sibilla: 'Is it true you called me *my love*?' 'You were trembling. You said such loving things to me.' 'Have you ever been loved, Dino?') Sitting on that same wall where he had waited for her on Thursday, Sibilla and Dino discuss the present and the immediate future, plan their lives. She works for the French Cultural Institute in Florence: translations, nothing more. She has a relationship with a boy of seventeen, that same Raffaello Franchi to whom Dino had a few months earlier sold a copy of *Canti Orfici*: she'll break it off immediately, tomorrow. For his part, Dino has no relationships, never has had any all his born days, but has no intention of cutting a poor figure and brings up his 'Russian woman' in Scarperia who keeps plaguing him, won't let him be... 'So,' says he, 'I've decided to move up higher and further away, to Casetta, above Firenzuola. It's a matter of days now. Tomorrow or the next day I'm going to have a look at the rooms.' – In an undertone, he gravely confides to her his great secret (to which Sibilla, there and then, does not give much weight). 'I'm ill,' he tells her, 'I have an illness connected with the war, which began with the war. When the war ends, I'll no longer exist.'

Dino and Sibilla see each other again at Barco for the Ferragosto holiday (Sibilla: 'Among the great forests... will you wait for me? I'll make you cry out with joy when we take each other once more') and then spend three weeks together at Casetta di Tiara, now simple Casetta: four buildings and a campanile on a stony landscape sliced in two by a road – State Highway No 65 from Florence to Bologna – along which the articulated lorries cruise night and day, without a shop or a bar or a telephone booth. Many things must have been different up there at the beginning of the century if there were even picture postcards of 'Casetta di Tiara'. There was certainly a drinking-house, perhaps even an inn. Blue flax flowers peeped out from among the rocks, sheep grazed everywhere and the lads tending them would gather in noisy throngs. In place of television sets, there were stars. (Sibilla: 'The stars around Casetta.' Dino: 'Our stars. *Nos étoiles.*') But these are digressions. On the mountains above Firenzuola, outside time, Dino and Sibilla live their fragment of 'the everlasting hour'. They read, talk, gather mushrooms in the woods, make love wherever they please. A couple of times he is delirious at night; wanders round the house clutching his head between his hands and complaining of a wind blowing out there in the valley or else there inside him: a chill, 'hibernal' wind... About halfway through September Sibilla returns to Florence and Dino is left to face his nightmares alone. A bad line from a sonnet written by Giovanni Cena for Sibilla rings in his head like a tolling-bell: 'I discovered her and called her name Sibilla.' He is plagued by jealousy, which is in the forefront of his new deliriums and absorbs into itself all his previous fixations. The same thought that Callimachus had had: 'I who hate vulgar poetry and do not travel by the roads that everyone else follows; I who don't even drink at the fountains because I don't like public amenities; I am now compelled to share my love with other men.' ('But Callimachus at least,' reflects Dino, 'did not share his love with all the other poets of the Palatine Anthology!') During his growingly frequent and growingly anguished nocturnal deliriums, Sibilla has belonged, still belongs, to everybody: to Papini, to Prezzolini, to Soffici, to Boine, to Carrà, to Cardarelli, to all the ones at the front and to the boys who are not off yet because they're under age, those of fifteen, sixteen, seventeen, like Franchi... She is the harlot image of the national literature, the refuse bin of every brand of rhetoric, a feminine D'Annunzio: and he, Dino Campana, has let himself be taken in by such a mirage! He runs to his mirror, beats himself. 'It's all sorcery, idiot!' 'To each man she appears as the loved one!'

At the end of September, walking through woods that are already taking on their autumnal hues and across meadows full of meadow-saffron, Dino goes down to Marradi. From there he catches the train to Florence. He meets Sibilla at the station and proposes that they should go straight on to Pisa. 'Let's go to the sea-side, Sibilla.' 'Carrying no mental or any other useless baggage.' 'Let's clear out of this nest of creeps which is Florence.' She barely manages to persuade him to wait until the following morning. On Sunday 1 October Sibilla and Dino are at Marina di Pisa: they rent a villa in which, as the landlady would have it, D'Annunzio has stayed. That evening Dino is unwell. He is delirious, accuses Sibilla of wanting to 'novelize' him for the benefit of her other lovers, of exerting some kind of hypnotic influence on him... On Tuesday he feels better and pays a visit to his uncle in town. Sibilla seizes this opportunity to write to Cecchi, whose brother-in-law is a psychiatrist, enquiring 'what could he be given to calm him down, particularly at night, but without affecting his heart.' On Wednesday and on Thursday the scenes recur with increasing intensity: until, during the night between Saturday and Sunday, a battered Sibilla flees to the house of some fishing folk nearby, who are all for calling in the police. 'No, please,' she begs them. 'There's no need to send for anybody.' (In a fury after her admission that she really has had an affair with Papini, Dino has spat in her face and begun pummelling himself and her.) She goes back to Florence and stays with a friend, Contessa Ester Castiglioni. Here Emilio Cecchi comes to see her black eye, so she says, and beseeches her to 'break off all relations with Dino'. She gives her formal promise: she won't see him again. But when Dino cables her from Marina di Pisa ('Your presence required urgently come Campana'), Sibilla's only concern is only that she should not be seen with her black eye; that she should be beautiful for him...

Dino and Sibilla move out of Marina di Pisa and go to Casciana Terme, where she takes the waters against arthritis. Between Sibilla's immersions they furiously make love and as furiously quarrel. Dino, who is now genuinely 'mad', alternates between moments of relative lucidity and others of total insanity. He is tortured by migraine, particularly at night, and by obsessive deliriums. He charges Sibilla ('incarnation of the evil female soul') of having ensnared him with carnal love so as to rob him of that 'pure poetic accent' which he alone, in Italy, possesses; of wanting to prostitute 'the pure spirit of Italian poetry' to her lovers – Papini, Prezzolini, Soffici, Cena, Marinetti, Boine, Bastianelli, Carrà... He doesn't strike her, as he did in Pisa, but keeps her at arm's length, addresses her icily, using 'voi': 'Do not touch me, impure woman!' 'As I have already indicated to you, I do not intend to degrade myself any further with your loathsome embraces!' But Sibilla is not to be overawed. She practises 'carnal love' with determination and with fairish results for about ten days (during which time he sends postcards to friends and acquaintances saying that he is a gigolo, that he's living with a slut, that he's set himself up as the ponce of a well-known whore). On Wednesday 25 October, Dino presents Sibilla with an alternative: either she writes immediately to Bastianelli, Cardarelli, Soffici, Boine, Marinetti & Co saying that she no longer wants to have anything to do with them, or he leaves. Sibilla refuses, and Dino leaves. He goes to Marradi to ask his father for a few lire, then returns to Florence. They meet again on 2 or 3 November and go to stay in Settignano in the house of a Swedish lady journalist, Anstrid Anhfelt; they remain there, making love and exchanging blows like crazy, until Christmas Eve. (Anhfelt: 'They fought and clawed all night. They'll kill each other, for sure, unless someone intervenes.' 'My peace is shattered.' 'All night long in fear of something serious happening. The whole business is so revolting.')

By Dino's wish, they spend Christmas in Marradi, the only guests of Albergo Lamone. The gaunt horse-chestnuts along the short avenue, the musty smell in the hall, the chest-of-drawers and the iron bedstead in the room over-looking the railway present to Sibilla such a melancholy milieu that she longs for the contrast of her friends' house in a great city full of lights and shopfronts. But Dino persists in showing her the nondescript buildings of his nondescript town: the town hall, the school, his home (his parents being away in Siena, at his brother's)... Marradi looks deserted. Few people, mostly elderly, are about; shuttered windows conceal eyes eager to see what the 'madman' is up to, whom he's with. What 'the madman's wife' looks like. (And Sibilla's unease is in part a reflection of this sense of being under observation, of being spied upon; of being a *dramatis persona* in someone else's drama.)

The year 1916 comes to an end with more hitting and spitting. Dino makes off to Leghorn, it is not clear why. Sibilla takes refuge in her friend Castiglioni's house. At this distance from one another, they declare their love. (Dino: 'I love and will love Sibilla with the best part of myself.' Sibilla: 'I adore you. I live because you said you hold my love dear.') What is new now is that during his lucid moments he realizes that he is mad and asks her to help him. How? Sibilla turns to people she knows and even to Dino's mother, who sends with her reply a picture of Our Lady of Grace. She says: There's nothing to be done, he's been that way since he was fifteen. Someone (possibly la Castiglioni, perhaps Cecchi's brother-in-law, the psychiatrist Gaetano Pieraccini) discusses the Campana-Aleramo affair with Professor Tanzi, who holds the chair of psychiatry at the University of Florence. Dino, he is told, must be helped to recover his reason, or, if that is not possible, Sibilla must be helped to break with him so as not to end as he has. 'Right,' replies the celebrity, 'send the two of them to me together, and I'll see what can be done.' During the week before last of January 1917 (possibly Monday the 21st or Tuesday the 22nd, Tanzi examines Campana but makes no diagnosis because, he says, 'the neurasthenia he is suffering from is not itself the morbid phenomenon but only a symptom of it.' He advises immediate admission into a psychiatric clinic: he does not pronounce on the duration of treatment required, but warns that complete elimination of the affliction will take months, perhaps years. He vetoes staying by the seaside. ('I've been told that you've recently been staying in Leghorn: you must leave.') He recommends a mountain climate instead: in fact specifies the Alpine climate. ('The Apennines are in the Mediterranean and maritime zone.') He writes out some prescriptions and dismisses him. Then has la Aleramo shown in. And, naturally, I'm freely reconstructing these conversations, as there are no records or other evidence as to what Tanzi says to Sibilla, *tête-à-tête* and in the privacy of his consulting-room. We know only that after their interview Sibilla and Dino part immediately and definitively. Therefore I imagine Tanzi says to Sibilla: 'Dear and excellent lady. I've examined your friend Campana and I must inform you (confidentially, of course) that his form of neurasthenia is probably related to a degenerative infection of a pestilential kind, as is also indicated by his slight limp, by the cast in his right eye and by the appearance in the past, by his admission, of pimples and rashes all over his body... I don't know whether you follow my meaning... Years ago, Signor Campana contracted syphilis, and he is still affected by it. This is the cause of his neurasthenic disorders, to cure which he will need a long period of confinement and treatment. But now it is you we must concern ourselves with, unpleasant though the business may seem and, indeed, is... It is necessary to carry out thorough checks so as to establish whether you too have suffered infection and whether you are a carrier. And further, it is necessary, I'm sure you'll understand, to break off this relationship, of which no good can come, either for yourself or for your friend... I speak to you as I would to a daughter. The pangs of love are nothing compared to those of syphilis.'

Sibilla uses her small last remnant of lucidity to 'liquidate' Dino. She makes him write to his friends of *La Gazzetta del Popolo* asking them whether he can stay in their villa in Rubiana; she secures a small sum of money for him from a Florentine patron of the arts, Gustavo Sforni. She also wishes to write him letters of introduction to eminent Turinese cultural personalities – the novelist-critic Borgese and the poet-critic Thovez – but he flies into a rage, accuses her of wanting to corrupt him through her lovers, of having lovers all over the world... The scenes between them during their last few days together, now deprived of the corrective of 'carnal love', make them find each other hard to bear, which eases their parting. Dino leaves swearing that he'd take his own life rather than live with her again; Sibilla swears no oaths, but has already made her decisions. Late in January 1917, Dino returns to Marradi: from there, holding a certificate from the hospital and a permit from the *carabinieri*, on the second or third of February he goes to Bologna and catches the train to Turin. The white wastes of snow remind him of the day of his first escape, all those years ago. ('What's become of Regolo?') The sky is grey. The stations are thronged with soldier-boys, buried inside their winter uniforms that make them look even younger than they are. On the walls, on the sides of railway carriages, everywhere tricolor posters salute 'the lads of '99' on their way to the front. Turin, the city where two years earlier he had yelled out the newspaper headlines, now appears mournful and empty to Dino: a maze of streets criss-crossing at right angles and leading nowhere... He spends the night at the Albergo dell'Agnello and by the evening of the following day has already reached the Val di Susa, to stay in a cold, empty house close to Rubiana but within the Almese district limits. (The old folk in Rubiana say that in the early part of the century there were as yet few villas in their mountains; that the 'Villa Irma' where the poet stayed has certainly changed its name and is, in all probability, the one which is still to be seen on the road which comes up from Almese, almost at the boundary between the two districts. The earliest proprietors within living memory are a Turin family called Rosa with interests in Fiat; but the person who told me this also said there was no knowing whether the villa actually belonged to the Rosas during the Great War.)

Whether from the effect of the climate or of the medicine prescribed by Tanzi, Dino feels himself coming back to life in the mountains of Piedmont: his migraines diminish, his obsessive ideas do not entirely disappear but remain, so to speak, in the background; the fog lifts from his mind, his interests and inclinations return to what they always used to be. On sunny days he strolls through the forests; he reads, writes, plans to set up a journal, 'The Diary of the New Italy', which, he says, is to be 'a paper devoted to European culture and addressed to everybody'. 'This paper, which should appear twice a month, should bring together the most important of the articles which have recently been published, showing their relevance to the present. Everything important in our national life (for example, Leopardi's life in its real significance) has been overlooked or related to events of that time which are too petty. The journal would have the character of an intellectual newspaper, with a leading article and a *faits divers* column. No criticism and no art.' Even the memory of Sibilla is not too tormenting and then there's his 'little love-affair' with his 'poppet', there's a genteel country girl, Rubiana's equivalent to the poet Gozzano's Signorina Felicita, with whom he acts 'the heart-broken lover'...

From Villa Irma, which looks out over the valley of the Dora, during April of 1917, Dino walks up to Rubiana every day and into the vicarage garden where a girl – the parish priest's niece – sews and listens to his stories about the countries he has visited, about the numbers and numbers of jobs he's done to survive: the policeman's, the usher's, the triangle-player's, the shooting-gallery attendant's, the tinker's, the labourer's, the stoker's . . . She's a slightly 'fat' young woman with 'almond eyes', a 'churchy beauty' on whose account he affects an arch smile but about whom he can not be quite indifferent if he also says that he will remember her 'for a good long while': 'For a good long while I'll remember / That girl whose eyes / Are aware and sad and tranquil / And who wears a conventional hat.'

Seeing that Dino is tranquil, Sibilla launches into tormenting him with fiery letters ('Dino, I and you have loved as
no one could have loved more, as no one will ever be able
to love more') and also writes to his mother Fanny, who
replies on 22 March enclosing a picture of St Francis and
urging them to 'legalize the union'. Dino cables 'come
immediately'; she says no, I won't come, but blurts out 'I
love you still'. On 24 April he makes a trip to Lake Avigliana
with his Signorina Felicita; sends Sibilla a card addressing
her in the distant second person plural: 'Life is a vicious
circle. Are you sending translations?' She replies by return
of post: 'I am thine. Adieu.' Dino rushes to Florence to look
for her (this is early May); she goes to stay in Milan and
from there writes 'letters of heart-rending passion'. 'Anyway,' she says, 'you'll never find me.' A certain Futurist
etcher, Filippo Marfori, rebukes her sternly: 'If you've
wanted to elude Campana and if we've helped you do so,
that is precisely because up to now he has caused you to
suffer, but if, now that you're away, you excite his emotions, which are already excited enough by the urge to discover your hiding-place, then that is not only a dangerous
game but, quite frankly, not one in which you should
involve your friends.' Dino manages to get hold of a hotel
address and cables: 'I ardently desire to see you.' She flees
to Varese to stay at the villa of her friends the Tallones;
from there she moves to Ca' d'Ianzo, a hamlet of a few
families on the slopes of Mont Rose. She is beginning to

find the 'state of sanctity' prescribed by the doctors somewhat trying, and this is probably why she badgers Dino,
who in her eyes is the cause of it all. On 20 June she writes
to him, possibly from Varallo Sesia: 'Tomorrow I press on
up the high valley. There are so many valleys in the Alps.
You can't guess which one I'm in. The aim would be to
stay at least three months, which, added to the five already
spent in a state of sanctity, would be a record.'

Dino sees Marradi once more ('Here, hay smells along
the valleys to infinity! So lovely!') and then returns to
Rubiana: but he does not regain there either the idyll with
his 'poppet' nor the advantages of the treatment prescribed
by Tanzi. His nightmares return; his delirious mirages
superimpose themselves on reality and, little by little,
supplant it. In Marradi again in August, he alternates
between depressive crises in which he designs his tomb and
converses with toads addressing them by his own name
('Poor Dino. Don't stay there in the middle of the road.
You'll be squashed') and moments of Futurist elation:
'Among all the modern aeroplanes mine too will pursue its
destiny. Death or glory!' He signs himself: 'Dino Campana
/ so-called / Poet of the present and of the future.' Early in
September, he goes to Florence. He rents the room which
Sibilla had had on the Lungarno Acciaioli and writes to her
at the Milan hotel, which forwards her mail on to her: 'I'm
in your room. Tell me whether it should see me live or
die.' The letter reaches Sibilla at Ca' d'Ianzo and – as she's
packing her bags to go away – plays a trick on him, 'inad-
vertently' writing back to him on the pensione's headed
notepaper (*Pensione Alpi – Ca' d'Ianzo – Novara*). She pre-
empts her friends' remonstrations, writing to Cecchi, for
instance, on 9 September 1917: 'I've written back just a few
lines to Campana, on parting and courage. Any other yarn
he might spin to you is his own invention.' (But the autumn
lines 'on parting' are not included in the Campana-Aleramo
correspondence which was published in 1958 with Aleramo's
approval: nor, for that matter, are her spring lines of 'heart-

rending passion'.) Dino receives her letter on the morning of the tenth: that same evening he is in Novara. He lodges in an inn beside the railway station. During the night he is delirious: 'I alone,' he cries, 'am responsible for this strife, for these horrendous massacres. But after my meeting with Sibilla the cycle will be closed.' The inn-keeper and his wife think they've come up against one of the numerous drop-outs and deserters whose minds have been unhinged by the war and send word to the police. On Tuesday, 11 September, at Novara railway station, Dino enquires as to how to get to Ca' d'Ianzo. 'It's at the edge of the world,' a clerk explains. 'You take the train to Varallo and then go on by coach. Unfortunately' – looking at his watch – 'the first train has left.' Faced by these complications, and sensing that he would not in any case get there in time to meet Sibilla, Dino gives up. He goes to the post office and cables her in Milan: 'I'm ill beg see you.' Then he returns to the station, and while he's studying the train timetable a police-man taps him on the shoulder and says: 'Hey, you. Just a word.'

After an hour's wait on the bench and half an hour's questioning, Dino is led away to prison in the Sforza castle at the city's edge; but he is first allowed to despatch (or rather to have a warden despatch) two telegrams to Sibilla, one to her Milan address and one to Ca' d'Ianzo: 'Arrested Novara come see me Campana.' Sibilla gets the message, sees that her joke is turning sour and that it must be ended. She returns to Milan, where a lawyer called Enrico Gonzales writes her a letter of introduction to the Procurator Royal of Novara. With this in her bag, on Thursday 13 September she arrives in the 'unknown township': she takes a cab to the Law Courts and has lunch with the Procurator, talks to the police second-in-command, vouches for the identity of the person arrested for being without documents as being in fact the writer Dino Campana from Marradi, unfit for military service on account of nervous disorders and beside himself with love... The officer smiles. 'If it's a matter of love...' 'Tomorrow,' he promises, 'I'll send him back home with a compulsory order. But only on one condition: that you go into the prison and identify him.' Sibilla hedges, but the policeman is adamant. 'It's a necessary step,' he says. 'I must be certain that the person released is the right one and no other.'

This last meeting, in prison, is already a meeting between strangers. For Dino, though he tries to kiss her hands through the bars, Sibilla is now simply the sum total of his fixations, past and present. For her, annoyed and disappointed, Dino is nothing but a 'lunatic' deserving of every chastisement. ('For the bruises which the lunatic left upon my white limbs, which I stared at, smarting, astonished, and he sneered sinisterly shrill and kept adding insults and spitting. For the rose crushed along my garment's hem. I who was life' etcetera.) On Friday 14 September Dino takes a walk along the Novara 'rampart' facing the sunlit Alps. Within twenty-four hours he must present himself before the *carabinieri* in Marradi but he's in no hurry. He feels well: 'The sharp wine has heartened me / And from the rampart boundless / Azure / Pauses over the birches, / Aerial Pantheon of columns / Above a garden in Lombardy. / Sun-dense September / Where the birches emerge in the / Plain / Far away remain / White crags.' He watches, entranced, the swallows darting around the cupola of San Gaudenzio: 'Before the columned arcade / Scored in the azure perse dartings / Quiver.'

That evening Dino is in Milan. He looks for Sibilla in her hotel and naturally doesn't find her as she is with the Tallones in Varese. He runs into the poet Cardarelli and the two of them together end up in Carrà's studio, where Dino becomes delirious (by this time he is delirious every night). He keeps repeating the usual phrases: 'My love for Sibilla is what's caused the war', 'The cycle is about to close'... Cardarelli, who in the not-so-distant past has also had an affair with Aleramo, shoots to his feet. 'The company's fine,' he says, 'but I'm tired of listening to this balderdash.' He picks up his hat and walking-stick and then from the doorway turns back, looking at Dino, who has fallen silent. He yells at him: 'I've known you addled. Now you're rotten.' He repeats, tapping his forefinger on his temple: 'D'you follow me? You're rotten! Rotten!'

While at Lastra a Signa with his father, Dino receives from Binazzi the offer of a job with *Il Mattino* as a proof-reader: he replies that he's unwell and can't live away from home. He goes into Florence every day, on foot. With one eye fixed and with his hobbling gait he wanders around a city which is aghast at the ever more grim reports from the front. He enters the 'Pilsen' beerhouse in Piazza Strozzi, where some young fellows (Nerino Nannetti, Spina, Remo Chitti, Primo Conti) are telling tales of Futurism; he goes up to them, removes the tray with their drinks, mounts the table and harangues them, saying: 'Look at us now in the midst of war, a frightful, tragic war... Be it known to you that I am the culprit for this war, the cause of this war is my love-affair with Sibilla Aleramo...' (Conti: 'At first we'd taken it as a joke, then we realized he really meant it. Nerino Nannetti stole out, whether to telephone someone or to call a hospital I don't know... But Campana, once he'd uttered that declaration, so clear-cut and so anguished, cheered up, got off the table, replaced the tray, and sat down as if nothing had happened. Shortly after, he left, but all of us were left with the sensation that something had gone very seriously wrong in our friend's mind: the first sign of his vanishing once and for all from our lives...')

On 19 October he is admitted to the Maglio military hospital, where he's been called for a check-up. This is the eve of the Italian military disaster of Caporetto and the hospital is overflowing with the semi-blind, the maimed, the deaf, the genuinely or purportedly insane, the young men claiming to be suffering from a weak heart or tuberculosis or diabetes... Dino is kept under observation for over a month, until the end of November; more than once during this period he forgets where he is and wants to leave. He is plagued by two obsessions: his love for Sibilla Aleramo and Beethoven's last words: 'The south of France, that's where, that's where.' (He cries: 'I must leave!' 'I must go to Nice!') Definitively rejected for military service, he tries to persuade his mother Fanny to go to France with him. 'Let's go to Nice,' he tells her. 'I'll work, I'll get better. The climate's wonderful there.' He drinks to excess, engages in public brawls. When he is summoned to the police station in December, he talks of a persecution campaign against him organized by some persons named Papini, Soffici, Prezzolini, Cecchi, Bastianelli, Cardarelli and Carrà. 'That lot', he says, 'want to destroy me through Sibilla Aleramo, the twenty-cent woman.' He reaches into his pocket and displays a coin. 'This louse', he explains to the policemen who are busy nodding and winking at each other, 'descended upon me like the divine wrath and has left me shattered in horror.' 'Yes, I know,' says the inspector, 'but if you don't stop causing uproars at night, I'll fix you up somewhere which will make you pine for the time when your enemies were persecuting you.' On 16 December he decides on suicide and writes various farewell notes, then forgets about it. On Christmas Day he is still lucid enough to wax indignant over an umpteenth 'appeal to the Italians' by Gabriele D'Annunzio. 'I haven't been able to read the speech by the *Vate*. He's too much of a littérateur even at the best and the worst of moments. It seems to me that he is the *cloaca maxima* of all the literary filth past and present of all continents and I am not inclined to discover myself in his speeches.' Early in January he calls on Anna, 'the Russian woman', from Scarperia, and makes her write raving messages in French to be later sent off to certain friends of Sibilla's. These messages, showing a triangle drawn at the foot, all say: 'Sir. My friend charges me to write you these things whose meaning I do not comprehend. The cycle which encloses the Italian war and which opened four years ago being now concluded, the man still living requests the go-between to see once more the lady with whom he wants to live. He promises to be faithful to her and to her friends in the Fourth Italy. △.' On 12 January 1918, in Lastra a Signa, he chases a boy down the street; the boy bolts inside his father's cobbler's shop and locks the door. Dino batters on it with a rock. People gather, the police arrive. Dino is frog-marched, struggling, to the medical officer, who makes out the form, and then to the town hall, where the Mayor signs the order committing him to an asylum. (Both these documents are lost.) By the evening of the same day Dino Campana is in San Salvi, shorn, deloused and in lunatic's uniform: that is, to quote the regulations, in 'hospital uniform made of brown wool with a round cap of the same material.' The tragedy of the last of the Germans in Italy (perhaps of the last of the poets) is – once and for all – concluded.

All that's left to be said concerns the 'lunatic'. On 13 January 1918 a certain Dr Delpiano, on behalf of the Director of the Florence Psychiatric Clinic, notifies 'the Most Illustrious Procurator Royal' that on the 12th Campana Dino son of Giovanni, born and domiciled in Marradi, was 'admitted and provisionally enrolled'. And again on the Director's behalf on 28 January Delpiano addresses the Procurator Royal: 'In fulfilment of the requirement to report on the mental condition of the patient named herein, from the Marradi Comune, admitted on 12 January 1918, I hereby inform Your Excellency that he is suffering from dementia praecox, wherefore I deem it necessary that he be permanently enrolled.' On 30 January 1918, Procurator Illegible, overstamped in blue ink, requests 'that the High Court pronounce the aforementioned lunatic permanently enrolled in the San Salvi Asylum'. Finally, on 18 March 1918, 'The Florence Civil and Criminal Court, Section II / Having seen the documents regarding Campana Dino of Giovanni and of Francesca Luti aged 32 unmarried born and domic. in Marradi / provisionally admitted to the Florence Lunatic Asylum / by the Mayor of Lastra a Signa by his order of 12 January 1918 as being affected by dementia praecox / And having seen the request by the Procurator Royal; / Whereas the aforementioned documents show the state of mind of the abovementioned Campana to be such as to necessitate his definitive admission to the aforementioned Asylum, while no improvement has resulted since he was temporarily admitted; / For these reasons / In view of art. 2 of Law of 14 February 1904 and relevant regulation 50 / Orders the transfer of the said Campana from temporary to permanent admission to the Florence Asylum. / So resolved in the Council Chamber on this day 18.3.1918 by the undersigned / Drs Spinosi, Cattai, Graziani. Chancellor: Illegible.'

The lunatic's physical description reads: 'Build, medium; chest and limbs, robust; hands, large; skin colour, pink; hair, tawny; general nutrition, good; face, square-set; cranium, round, balding in front; ears, regular; forehead, broad.' Pariani, going by the clinical record, writes, 'Examination of the nervous system revealed a disorder of the vascular nerves along the right-hand side of the face and along the hand on the same side.' After a brief stay at San Salvi, in the ward for disturbed patients, the patient is transferred to the asylum for chronic cases at Castel Pulci, in the district of Badia a Settimo. Here, according to Pariani, 'he at first showed signs of auditory hallucinations, expressed delusions of grandeur and persecution, was subject to unjustified outbursts. Subsequently false perceptions – auditory, cutaneous, muscular and visceral, sometimes painful, were prevalent; also representational delusions, thoughts repeated out loud; absurd notions of grandeur. Speech remained unaffected.' 'He appeared lucid with correct notions of time and place and without loss of memory, but uttered strange discourse from which he would let nothing distract him.' 'He read the newspapers, and the news, which he interpreted in his own way, increased his delirious ravings and ramblings. He ignored his fellow-inmates, avoided addressing them. He would pace up and down with a long, elastic stride, his neck and shoulders hunched up, his head slightly bowed, without looking around.'

The most regular of the lunatic's rare visitors is his mother, Fanny: who turns up by the morning coach, wrapped in her shawl, and asks him: 'How are you?' (Dino: 'How d'you expect me to be? Like someone in a lunatic asylum.') His guardian, Uncle Torquato, shows up once or twice a year; his brother Manlio's visits are even fewer and further between. His father, who is to die in 1926, never once sets foot in Castel Pulci, because 'he hasn't the heart'. Of the Florentine writers, only Ferdinando Agnoletti, in the first few months of 1918, turns up at the gate of San Salvi and asks to speak to 'the writer Campana': after a brief wait, a doctor appears and tells him that the patient in question is in no state to receive anybody. 'Tell me at least what he's doing,' Agnoletti insists. 'Is he reading? Or writing?' The doctor shrugs: 'Even if he wrote anything, he'd write things that made no sense...'

Once the irate outbursts and furies of the first few months are over, Dino Campana is already by the beginning of 1919 the model patient of whom doctors and orderlies talk admiringly. (Pariani: 'His emotions and his actions were peaceable and trivial...' 'He tolerated patients who were epileptic, idiots, insane, obtuse, unclean.') Yes, occasionally he is disturbed: he suffers from painful insomnia which makes him bad-tempered; he refuses, at first, to be 'plagued' with 'electrical stimuli'. But he is fond of the asylum and very happy to be living there, without responsibilities and without problems. And besides, he likes Castel Pulci. He likes the building, which used to be a residence of the Grand Dukes of Tuscany; he likes the park and the landscape... He will tell Pariani with feeling, when the latter questions him in 1927: 'It's a peaceful place where I'm very comfortable and I hope I don't leave it.'

His 'electric' deliriums begin in 1924 or 1925, more or less at the time when Italian psychiatrists discover shock therapy as the cure-all for neuroses, and they continue until 1930. 'I'm completely filled with magnetic currents,' says Dino. 'My name is Dino; as Dino, my name is Edison.' 'I can live even without eating, I'm electric.' 'I caught the attention of the Marconi police and they smashed my head. They hit me with a powerful electrical shock. I thought they'd ruptured a vein in my brain!' 'Wilson sent me a very strong electrical shock. It smashed my head! Special agents used to give me plenty of torture.' His mother complains of an infirmity, and he promises her a quick cure by electricity: 'I have the methd and the means,' he whispers to her, 'of curing humanity of all its ills... I only have to will it.'

Between one bout of shock therapy and the next, Dino Edison reads, makes meatballs for his fellow-inmates, and masturbates. He is happy. Lazzeri (a patient at Castel Pulci): 'During the day, when he was up among the other patients, he sat in a corner reading continuously!' Borghesi (another patient): 'He was always in with us; a reading man he was, a great reading man... He took his book into corners, leant against the wall and slid down and down to the ground... then he read on the ground... sitting on the ground...' Inspector Del Bene (medical): 'He was a bookish lad, gentle towards all the other patients. At one point he was assigned kitchen duties and he devoted himself to making meatballs. Then he'd go round among the patients and tell them, well, that he'd made these meatballs and he encouraged them to eat them: he advertised his meatballs. No one has ever tasted better in this place, it seems!' Borghesi: 'He was a good lad! A good lad! He used to read, but then afterwards...! A reading man, a great reading man, eh...! He used to write a little, too, and then, afterwards, he'd settle down there to read!... he even ruined his eyesight, poor fellow, so as to read!' Ugolini (orderly): 'He was an obedient man. He never raged. He was a good man who didn't question orders. When it was time to eat, he'd eat, when it was time to sleep, he'd sleep. I can't remember ever having strapped him to his bed as was often the case with other patients... I've never seen him coupling with others.' Orlandelli (orderly): 'I never found him coupling with others, nor was it ever necessary to strap him to his bed. His only vice, poor fellow, was masturbating...' Ugolini: 'What I can tell you because I've seen it with my own eyes is that Signor Campana used to masturbate like mad. And his cock was this size.' (Gesture.)

Only two disagreeable events disturb the serenity of Dino Edison in his hospital for chronic lunatics in Badia a Settimo. These events are, in order of importance: the appearance in his life of the psychiatrist Pariani; Vallecchi's commercial republication of the *Canti Orfici*.

Let's begin with Pariani. Carlo Pariani, psychiatrist, is not attached to Castel Pulci but comes over expressly to biographize Dino Edison, to subject him to a barrage of questions until 'his answers are slow in coming, and brief, his face turns red and sets hard, his upper eyelids droop, indicating fatigue.' Dino is absolutely uncomprehending as to the purport of such full enquiry: he thinks he might be driven out of the asylum on account of something he's done in the past, and he says as little as he can, always in vague terms, adding phoney details, back-tracking, toning things down. In hours and hours of interviewing Pariani never manages to extract from him a single first-hand memory, new detail or spontaneous remark. Only when he comments on the text of the *Canti Orfici* does Dino Edison say anything interesting, and still always circumspectly, trying to anticipate what his interrogator wants: what is he after? Censoring the more scandalous pieces? Fine. He's in complete agreement, as long as afterwards he's left in peace... 'The night-whores down at the crossroads: Dino disapproves of them and defines them as – oddities.' 'The lady in love with his faun-eyes, when he hears her once more, he flushes; and exclaims: – that's not true at all, just fantasies!'

'He displays scorn in his countenance and in his voice, laughs with contempt on listening to the smutty image of "the old whores", he disapproves without making excuses: – "Drunk's talk. Should be censored."'

During his first meetings with the lunatic, Pariani tries to ingratiate himself by bringing him the odd pack of cigarettes ('Campana enjoyed smoking but lacked money to procure it') and by promising to enable him to meet his literary friends. Dino Edison looks at him in horror. 'For goodness' sake,' he says, 'I have no wish to meet anybody. I beg you to understand that I'm all right as I am.' 'His behaviour,' notes Pariani, 'during those two meetings and subsequent ones, was that of someone who would rather sidestep questions and maintain his independence.' But Pariani persists and so Dino Edison tells him roundly to desist, as anyway he's understood perfectly what his aim is: 'You're sent here by the Government to find out whether I want to leave this place; but I don't. You've been prompted to come and see me, because you have no interest in getting to know me. You represent the King of Italy, who wants to send me to Florence, whereas I have no wish to go there.'

Could anything be clearer...? Yet Pariani continues to seek him out, to write to him, and so (this is the spring of 1927) Dino Edison takes pen and paper and replies: 'I have no business or ties in Italy. I wouldn't know what to say to you about my past literary activity which was slender and fragmentary. It is not important enough for you to take the trouble to come and see me. I lead a tranquil life.'

The persecution goes on for three and a half years, from November of 1926 to April of 1930. During this period Dino exerts himself to the utmost to give away as little as possible about himself and to put off that tiresome individual in every possible way. Repeatedly in his letters he asks to be left in peace; not to receive visits. 22 October 1927: 'My life follows a normal course in this place. I beg you not to trouble yourself coming to see me because I'm fine.' 22 October 1929: 'I don't wish to see anyone. I'm used to this life, I don't wish to change it.' 11 April 1930: 'I do not wish to change, nor to have visitors, nor to get out.'

The new *Canti Orfici* that arrives in the Italian bookshops with the ink hardly dry at the end of 1928 is a reprint carried out by the personal wish of the publisher Attilio Vallecchi: the same who in 1914 rubbished Campana's typescript, keeping only the covering letter. ('Esteemed Signor Vallecchi, I am writing to you in the hope that you will take an interest in my case.') Now that Dino is inside Castel Pulci, Vallecchi collects what he published here and there, in little and not so little journals (*Riviera Ligure, La Tempra, La Teda, La Brigata, La Voce*); he cleanses the Marradi edition of those writings which are unbecoming to the dignity of his firm (the tragedy of the last of the Germans, the dedication to Wilhelm II, the epigraph about the boy's blood); he makes a single package of the whole lot and then approaches the illustrious (Papini Prezzolini Soffici), asking for a preface: but he encounters unexpectedly difficult obstacles. In particular, Prezzolini tells him that Dino is 'a by-product of D'Annunzianism'; Papini, that he's 'a second-rate poet'; Soffici passes no adverse judgement but hints that, when all's said and done, the sun shines on better things... Only the less illustrious Binazzi responds with enthusiasm to Vallecchi's invitation and he gives the monster (that is, Dino) a banner headline: quite convinced in all good faith that he's doing the monster (his friend) an inestimable service. Dino, says Binazzi, is, first of all, a madman: immured as such in an asylum where 'he writes and writes'. However, as long as his madness permitted, he was also a circus performer, a charlatan, travelled all the continents, practised every trade, experienced the world of Lady Misery, spoke every language, knew every brothel... – With everything set and ready for the press, the madman's guardian, Torquato, signs the publishing contract; and the result of all this hustle and bustle is that one winter's morning around the end of 1928 or the beginning of 1929 Dino Edison receives through the post a book carrying his name: 'Dino Campana. *Canti Orfici*'. Then and there, he is not greatly struck (Papadía, a doctor: 'He no longer attached any importance to his poetic work') but later he begins leafing through the volume during his lucid moments: he notices the errors, the cuts, the arbitrary inclusion of poems which had taken shape in a different context and, though as from a great distance, he registers this last great wrong. He writes to his brother begging him to 'look for the original Marradi edition, so as to keep it in memory'. Otherwise, he says, 'the text will be lost' (2 June 1930).

So the years go by at Castel Pulci: among idiots and degenerates who copulate together, who howl strapped to their beds, who shit and piss themselves, who masturbate... Until, by various accounts, in November 1931 Dino Edison's mind begins to clear, to manifest 'wishes plans acts such as we observe in the sane'. He requests grammar-books in the languages he knows: he attempts to translate from the German and is pleased with the result. For the first time in thirteen years he voices the desire to leave the asylum, to find himself a job as a translator or interpreter. 'But', the doctors object, 'your occupation was writing.' Dino flushes: 'No, no...' 'I no longer wanted to engage in literary affairs given the nil practical success I've achieved.' 'The book market in Italy is absolutely null as regards my line of writing.' He continues practising his foreign languages and those in charge at Castel Pulci consider releasing him during 1932. In particular, the inspector, Del Bene, speaks of him as someone who has recovered: 'He was relaxed and peaceable, even at night, during his last months; looking well-fed and fresh. He dressed neatly. He seemed rather shy. Perfect manners, really. He kept himself rather to himself: he would reply when asked a question; very well-mannered, kind. He always read the newspapers. He used to chat to Dr Faberi about current topics.'

Death comes suddenly and unexpectedly. At the beginning of February 1932 Dino falls ill and dies – according to his brother – in mysterious fashion: 'After an illness lasting twelve hours and a death-agony lasting six hours, without interruption.' More detailed is the account by Pariani, who has access to the patient's clinical record and transcribes it as follows: 'On the 27th he comes into the infirmary with a fever and in a fairish overall condition. On the 28th his temperature was slightly over 38 degrees and a widespread rash appeared, with bright red, but not swollen, blotches. Then his fever mounted to over 40 degrees and remained high, with oscillations. An oedematous infiltration of the genital organs was observed; the skin in the genital area and on the lower limbs was covered with reddish patches. His appearance was that of someone seriously ill: his face ashen, his tongue dry, he was sweating, vomiting, he had diarrhoea, his senses were dulled; his hands were twitching, he was delirious and restless. He realized he was close to death and said to the infirmarian: "Save me, Setaioli, I'm dying." He expired at a quarter to twelve, midday, on the first of March at the age of forty-six, after fourteen years in the asylum.' The diagnosis indicates 'acute primary septicaemia' caused by Dino's wounding his genitals with a rusty iron object; or, alternatively, 'a direct and virulent microbic infection of the blood': which is a roundabout way of saying 'plague', 'cholera'. In fact, the doctors at Castel Pulci don't know the cause of the inmate Campana's death, and fear an epidemic: so they order the immediate interment of the body in the nearest cemetery. ('*Inspector Del Bene*: When he died, Signor Campana was taken to Badia over there, straight to the cemetery; straight there! *Zavoli*: Can we see it, from this window? *Inspector*: We should be able to see it from the window... Yes, over there! Over there! The *palazzone*! The *palazzone* without a campanile, can you see it? That's where the cemetery is.') Dino gets there towards four o'clock in the afternoon on that same first of March, 1932, in a Fiat hearse driving at normal speed: no one is following the coffin, in any case... (Not his family from Marradi, who arrive the following day, nor the publisher Vallecchi, nor his beloved Sibilla who – according to a legend which blossomed during the Seventies, the period of her feminist beatification – 'kept visiting him incognito until his death in 1932...')

So assured is Pariani that the memory of the subject of his biography will be ephemeral, that he makes the prognostication that Campana's bones will cease to occupy a grave after the minimum period of ten years set down by law: 'In 1942 his remains, unless somebody claims them, will be scattered so that they will feed pure grasses; these, animals; and these, man, whose remains are nowadays seldom relished by his fellows. Fire transmutes them into rich ash which floats gently down to earth or they are browsed upon by worms which do not elude transformation into nitrogenous powders, an excellent fertilizer.' But Campana's fame develops in an exactly opposite way to that of his more celebrated contemporaries, who today are discussed in degree theses and tomorrow will be discussed no more. In 1942, thanks to a public subscription by artists and admirers, the poet's remains are transhumed into the little Romanesque church of the Badia cemetery. The Minister of Culture, Bottai, comes to Florence for the occasion: his presence confers on the ceremony, to be frank, an excessively official character, and helps to fuel the misconception – to which ill-informed and illustrious people such as P.P. Pasolini will fall a prey – of Campana as a 'precursor of Fascism', and also attracts the presence of at least one superfluous person, Papini. 'I can still see, as through a freezing mist, [the poets] Gatto and Montale raise the small chest containing Campana's remains and lay it upon the altar for inhumation. And then Rosai and Carlo Bo, still boyish-looking, adorn his tomb with a simple laurel wreath: the simplest that could be found. Papini was standing next to Bottai' (Primo Conti). Was he really praying, as Conti suggests, or was he hatching that article 'Pazzi in rialzo' (Lunatics Rising), in which, a few years later, he attempted once again to discredit the memory of the 'second-rate poet', of 'the lunatic' who had taken the liberty of flouting the literary circles of his day, their rituals and hierarchies? 'It seems to us,' Papini, now aged sixty-four, writes in this article, 'that the historical significance and the artistic value of the unhappy poet of Marradi is being ridiculously and dangerously overrated.' 'A detached examination of his work clearly demonstrates that his originality was slight – he'd absorbed a great deal of late nineteenth-century French literature – and that he can not be presented, except by tendentious fanatics, as an authentic or great poet.'

I get up to shut the window and am entranced by the view of the stars, or rather 'the magnetic glintings of the stars' which this evening speak to me also of the 'infinity of deaths'. They're all dead. All the characters in this story: the men of letters, the psychiatrists, the worthies of Marradi, the insane, the sane, the Futurists, the 'lads of 1899'... All of them. Alone, in the sky's abyss, Halley's Comet continues tirelessly to weave its orbitings almost to the very limits of space and time. In their books the astronomers write that this Comet traverses the solar system every seventy-six years, that it will reappear in 1986: and I am convinced that in the complicated harmony of the Universe there is a secret connection between Halley's Comet ('What bridge, mutely we asked, what bridge have we thrown upon infinity, that everything appears to us the shadow of eternity:') and the poetry of human beings; that every passage of the star is matched by the passage of a poet. A poet every seventy-six years... Not particularly great, nor famous, nor taken into serious consideration. A *boy*, a 'primitive' who traverses the world without meeting his contemporaries and is torn to pieces by the people who are closest to him: his family, the people he knew, his presumed *confrères*. '*They were all torn / and cover'd with / the boy's / blood.*'

Certainly, Papini is right. Dino Campana, judged by his yardstick, is not 'an authentic or a great poet'. But there's a phrase in the manuscript recovered from Soffici's cupboard (it had been there for sixty years, and had never left it) which is Dino's answer: 'Being a great artist means nothing: being a pure artist, that's what matters.' This phrase, the epigraph to the book, encapsulates 'Leopardi's life in its true meaning' and encapsulates also the life of Dino Campana, whose view of the greatness of poets it hints at. The great poet, Dino is saying, is a man who lives entirely within his own present and ends there: like Papini or D'Annunzio. He has no contemporaries scattered across all the ages, he has no dialogue with those that have gone before and those yet to be born. His shadow is no 'shadow of eternity'. He is, basically, an ordinary fellow; a chap who becomes a great poet just as someone else becomes manager of the Savings Bank, with a bit of application, a bit of talent and a bit of luck. History, books, are full of these great poets, busy employees of their Age, of their Sovereign, of their Publisher. But Dino's thought contains a future in which humanity will at last have understood that poetry can serve it only on one condition: that of being beyond time and its traffickings. A bridge upon infinity, a message delivered to those who do not exist by those who will never return...

I'm thinking about Leopardi, and about Campana. Leopardi locates poetry in the past and in mankind's infancy ('Poets were none save the ancients, and are now none save children, or those still in their early youth, and those moderns that are called such are but philosophers'): misled by the fact that the lapse of centuries generally eliminates the 'great' poets and promotes that of the 'primitives', the *boys*... Campana voices the hope that the 'pure artist', who has always been an exile in the present, may find a homeland in the future thanks to a shift in taste that will bring 'back into fashion' 'primitives' such as himself: but things aren't quite so simple. If humanity is to stop cannibalizing its 'pure artists', something other and more than aesthetic maturation is required. Contemporary people must learn – for example – to recognize the historical necessity of Monsieur François Villon and the irrelevance of the 'great artists' Jean Molinet, Meschinot de Nantes, Guillaume Crétin (these are real names). It is not just a matter of aesthetics. What is needed is a growth of civilization and culture which will lead humans to tolerate the existence, which today more than ever is considered aberrant, of people who embody 'the superior moral type'; which will stop them from nailing such persons to crosses, from decapitating them on scaffolds, from roasting them on pyres. From incarcerating them in insane asylums and gaols. From forcing them to take their own lives or cut themselves off from the world...

How many times has Halley's Comet crossed human skies?

Among the poets it has 'tracered' are Jesus Christ and Joan of Arc, François Villon and Tommaso Campanella, Gérard de Nerval and Friedrich Nietzsche (he too, like Campana, a victim of *Spirochaeta pallida*); to mention but a few. And all of a sudden I catch myself, here at the window of the Albergo Lamone with the stars of Marradi before me, thinking of the next poet, the one of 1986: 'He'll be a boy,' I tell myself. 'A bit primitive, like Dino. At odds with his contemporaries. He will have no luck with publishers and will be regarded as a madman, someone who has understood nothing about ordinary living. He'll come to grief: like him.' Naturally, I don't know his work, but I do know some of its assumptions. I know that his firmament, unlike this one in which 'friars and poets have made their den like worms', will be a firmament 'undefiled by the shadow of Any God'. I know that he will not fall into the trap of artistic theory; that he will not barter poetry for 'Machiavellianism, cerebral technique, bourgeois phrase-mongering'; that he will not presume to regenerate it 'by sheer loud-mouthedness'. (In anger, and in anguish, I ask: 'How could we, ourselves, have paid any heed, yet again, to the Papinis and the Sofficis of today?') I know he will not belong to any 'mob' of 'teenagers'; that he will feel, like Dino, that 'everything is a matter of individual effort'. Finally, I know that his ears and his heart will be full of 'the poetry of Italy that has been'. . .

It's late now. From the bar, which is right beneath my room, come drunken voices. Who knows how many times 'the madman' has been here. Who knows how many times the locals have offered him a drink so as to 'laugh' him down, all the way to Viale Baccarini, all the way to the Lamone bridge...

I turn on the light. The suitcase propped up against the radiator reminds me that the 'infinity of deaths' continues through my papers, that among the dead are now also the first of those to whom, thirteen years ago, I spoke of the 'Campana affair': Daniele Ponchiroli and Franco Basaglia, the psychiatrist who more than any other fought to change the asylum regime introduced in 1904. And, as is the custom, I should thank a hundred people: Italian cultural attachés abroad, mayors, parish priests, professors, writers, doctors, public order officers, archivists, artists, people who in various capacities have furthered my researches; I ought to validate what I have written by listing their names and titles. But I shall mention only one name, that of the Argentinian writer Gabriel Cacho Millet: who, enamoured of Campana's poetry, has spent part of his life tracing and publishing his letters. Without his care and pertinacity my imaginative biography of the poet would now be more uncertain: many episodes would be missing, many others would be left suspended 'in space, outside time'... To Gabriel Cacho Millet I am also indebted for some family memoirs and other unpublished evidence which he himself, with rare generosity, put at my disposal. Thanks. Other people, if I have not already done so, I shall thank privately. I wish above all to say that I do not feel myself to be a 'biographer', that in all probability I shall never again write a biography, either of a poet or of anybody else. I was looking for a character with a certain set of characteristics. Chance made me find him in historical reality, from which I've fished him out: doggedly, scrupulously, in a spirit of truth. (Though everything in the world is susceptible to further development, I don't think there's much more to discover about the poet Campana.) But even if Dino had never existed I would still have written this story and invented this marvellous and 'monstrous' man, I'm absolutely certain. This is how I would have invented him.

Final Note

Since *La notte della cometa* was published in Italy, documents have come to light (expulsion orders and police records) which enable us to date more precisely some of the incidents in the most obscure periods of the poet's youth, before he drafted and published the *Canti Orfici*. Qualified people have also explained to me that my use of the term 'electric shock therapy' towards the end of the book is inappropriate: in the 1920s electricity was used simply to inflict pain, without any therapeutic intent, so as to deter the patient from habits which were considered harmful, such as masturbation. The term 'electric shock therapy' was not yet in use, and the 'electrical stimuli' to which Pariani euphemistically refers must have simply been shocks administered to the poet's head or to his genitals. I could have corrected such blemishes in the text – blemishes which make no difference to the figure of Campana and its truth – with a few simple touches: but this seemed to me neither necessary nor even, upon due consideration, proper. 'A book', Nietzsche once wrote, 'is almost equivalent to a man': with a man's shortcomings and virtues, limitations and aspirations. It prompts new discoveries, provokes emotions and reactions, attracts more or less well-founded remonstration, and the author has no further right to intervene: 'For him, it is as though the severed segment of an insect were going its own way, on its own.'

– *Sebastiano Vassalli*

Translator's Note

The *Canti Orfici* are almost the sole monument left by the Italian Orpheus, Dino Campana, who was born in 1883 and was definitively confined to an insane asylum in 1918, after the fraught self-publication in 1914 of his book of free verse and prose poems. His poetic vocation took shape slowly, nurtured at first on the turn-of-the-century, aesthetic-leaning 'giants', Carducci, Pascoli and D'Annunzio, and the visionary-symbolist tradition of Poe, Baudelaire, Rimbaud, Verlaine, amidst the emotional and physical upheavals of a life in and out of boarding-schools, military academy, universities and mental institutions, Switzerland, Belgium, France and Argentina. A stranger in his own home and wherever he sought a home, he was not least a stranger in the pre-war Florentine avant-garde literary establishment: the circle centred around the literary Giubbe Rosse café which included the Futurists among its guests, under the literary dictatorship of the critics and writers Prezzolini, Papini and Soffici and the little magazines *Lacerba, Leonardo* and *La Voce*. Treated as a 'wild man' by this circle, bewildered by the outbreak of war between Germany and Italy, emotionally unbalanced by his love-affair with the writer Sibilla Aleramo (Rina Faccio), and overtaken by the effects of syphilis, Campana eventually found a 'home' in the insulated, structured world of the Castel Pulci asylum... He died suddenly, in 1932, just as he felt ready to step outside into 'normal' life. Death delivered him, for half a century, into the hands of his biographers – Pariani, Bejor, Gerola, Ravagli – who were not inclined to distinguish between clinical insanity and the social construct.

– John Gatt